PRIMARY MATHEMATICS
Standards Edition

TEXTBOOK

Yeap Ban Har

 **Marshall Cavendish** Education

 SingaporeMath.com Inc

Blank

© 2009 Marshall Cavendish International (Singapore) Private Limited

Published by Marshall Cavendish Education

An imprint of Marshall Cavendish International (Singapore) Private Limited

Times Centre, 1 New Industrial Road, Singapore 536196

Customer Service Hotline: (65) 6411 0820

E-mail: tmesales@sg.marshallcavendish.com

Website: www.marshallcavendish.com/education/sg

Distributed by

SingaporeMath.com Inc

404 Beavercreek Road #225

Oregon City, OR 97045

U.S.A.

Website: www.singaporemath.com

Marshall Cavendish Corporation

99 White Plains Road

Tarrytown, NY 10591

U.S.A.

Tel: (1-914) 332 8888

Fax: (1-914) 332 1082

E-mail: mcc@marshallcavendish.com

Website: www.marshallcavendish.com

First published 2009

ISBN 978-0-7614-2756-8

Printed in Singapore by Times Graphics Pte Ltd

PREFACE

The **chapter opener** introduces a topic in a fun and captivating manner that is sure to pique students' interest. The activities broaden students' thinking and allow much creativity in finding solutions to the questions posed.

 **(Standards Edition)** Grades 1 to 5 is a complete program from the publishers of Singapore's successful *Primary Mathematics* series. Newly adapted to align with the Mathematics Framework for California Public Schools, the program aims to equip students with sound concept development, critical thinking and efficient problem-solving skills. Grade 6 is written using the same pedagogy and mathematics framework for continuity.

Mathematical concepts are introduced in the opening pages and taught to mastery through specific learning tasks that allow for immediate assessment and consolidation.

The color patch [ ] is used to invite active student participation and to facilitate lively discussion about the mathematical concepts taught.

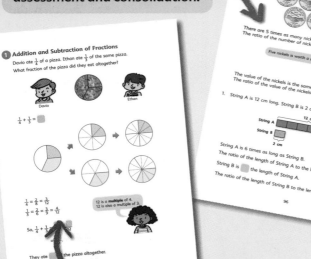

The Concrete → Pictorial → Abstract approach enables students to encounter math in a meaningful way and translate mathematical skills from the concrete to the abstract.

The **pencil icon** [Exercise 3, pages 11 - 12] provides quick and easy reference from the Textbook to the relevant Workbook pages. The **direct correlation** of the Workbook to the Textbook facilitates focused review and evaluation.

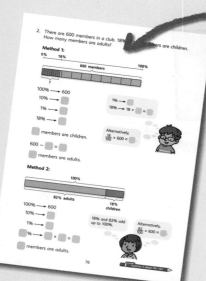

The **modeling method** enables students to visualize and solve mathematical problems quickly and efficiently.

New mathematical concepts are introduced through a **spiral progression** that builds on concepts already taught and mastered.

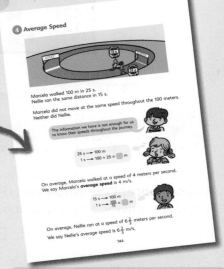

Regular **reviews** in the Textbook provide consolidation of concepts learned.

Metacognition is employed as a strategy for learners to monitor their thinking processes in problem solving. Speech and thought bubbles provide guidance through the thought processes, making even the most challenging problems accessible to students.

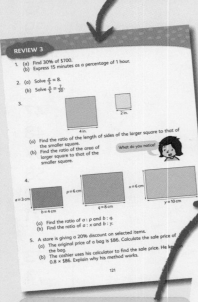

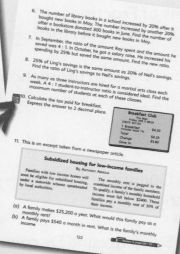

Questions with a **calculator icon** are introduced in Grade 6 to enable students to work out larger numbers in real-life situations.

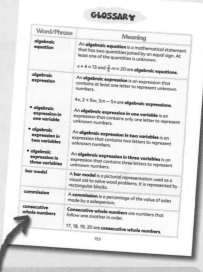

The **glossary** effectively combines pictorial representation with simple mathematical definitions to provide a comprehensive reference guide for students.

CONTENTS

Jeremy has five tiles numbered 1 through 5. He has to arrange the numbers such that they add up to the same number **horizontally** and **vertically**.

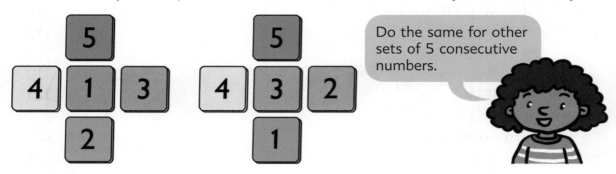

Do the same for other sets of 5 consecutive numbers.

Complete the table. The first one is done for you.

Numbers on tiles	Sum of numbers horizontally	Sum of numbers vertically	Number in the middle
1 to 5	8 9	8 9	1 3
2 to 6			
8 to 12			
20 to 24			

Is it possible to predict the numbers in the table without actually arranging the 5 numbers?

1 Algebraic Expressions I

The **table** below shows the number of apples each child has.

Amelia	Ben
1	4

The **model** also shows the number of apples each child has.

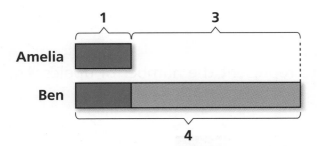

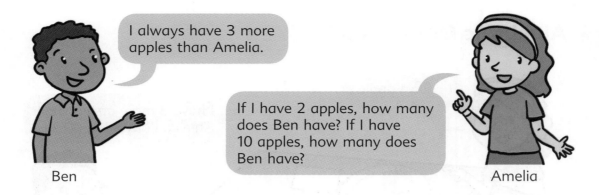

The table below shows the number of apples that Amelia has. Complete the table to find the number of apples that Ben has.

Amelia	Ben
1	$1 + 3 = 4$
2	$2 + 3 = \boxed{}$
10	$10 + \boxed{} = \boxed{}$
x	$\boxed{} + \boxed{}$

If Amelia has x apples, I have ⬚ apples.

We use this model to show the number of apples each child has.

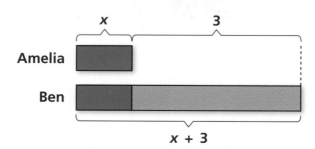

We can use x to represent the number of apples Amelia has.

10

1.

Complete the table.

Carl	Kimi
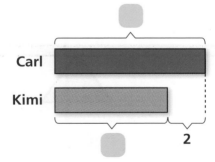	

Complete the model.

Exercise 1, pages 5 - 7

2.

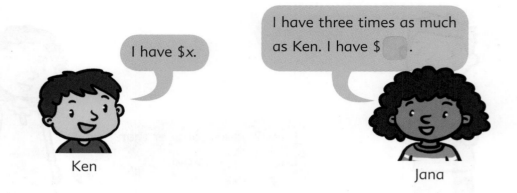

Complete the model.

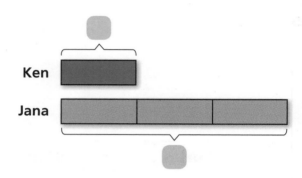

3. **Express** the weight of each baseball in terms of x.

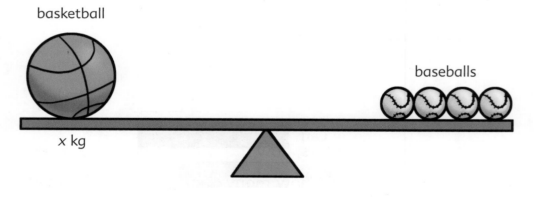

The weight of each baseball is ⬜ kg.

1. Earl has 4 more dimes than quarters.

    (a) If Earl has 10 quarters, how many dimes does he have?

    (b) If Earl has 10 dimes, how many quarters does he have?

    (c) If Earl has 10 dimes and quarters altogether, how many coins of each denomination does he have?

2. Ken has 4 more dimes than quarters.

    (a) If Ken has 12 quarters, how many dimes does he have?

    (b) If Ken has 12 dimes, how many quarters does he have?

    (c) If Ken has 12 dimes and quarters altogether, how many coins of each denomination does he have?

3. Anna has z fewer dimes than quarters.

    (a) If Anna has x quarters, how many dimes does she have?

    (b) If Anna has x dimes, how many quarters does she have?

    (c) If Anna has x dimes and quarters altogether, how many coins of each denomination does she have?

4. Sarah has 4 times as many dimes as quarters.

    (a) If Sarah has y quarters, how many dimes does she have?

    (b) If Sarah has y dimes, how many quarters does she have?

    (c) If Sarah has y dimes and quarters altogether, how many coins of each denomination does she have?

② Algebraic Equations

There are 6 more girls than boys in a class. How many girls are there if there are 12 boys in the class?

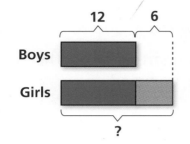

I know the number of boys. I can find the number of girls by adding 6 to 12.

$12 + 6 = 18$

There are 18 girls.

There are 6 more girls than boys in a class. If there are 30 children altogether, how many girls are there?

Method 1:

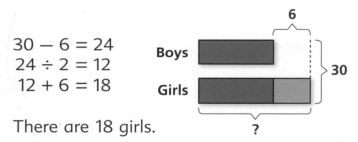

$30 - 6 = 24$
$24 \div 2 = 12$
$12 + 6 = 18$

I do not know the number of boys. How do I find the number of girls?

There are 18 girls.

Method 2:

Let the number of boys be x.

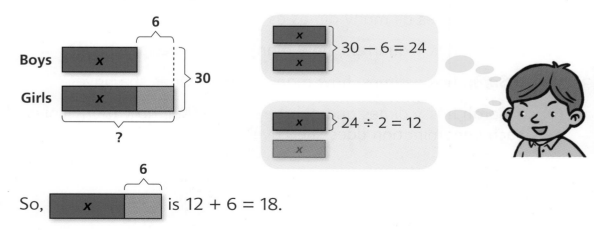

$30 - 6 = 24$

$24 \div 2 = 12$

So, ▭ is $12 + 6 = 18$.

There are 18 girls.

1. There are two numbers. The first number is 4 times as much as the second number.

   (a) If the second number is x, what is the first number in terms of x?

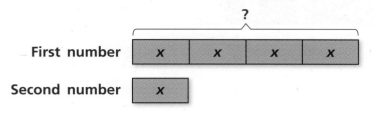

   The first number is ☐.

   (b) If the first number is 20, what is the second number?

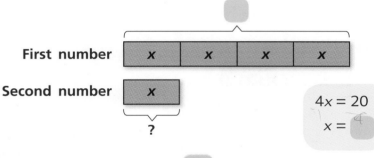

$4x = 20$

$x = $ ☐

   The second number is ☐.

2. Find the value of x when $3x = 15$.

   $3x = 15$

   $x = $ ☐

   15

   | x | x | x |

   ?

3. **Solve** $x + 3 = 15$.

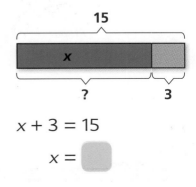

When we find the value of x, we **solve** the equation.

What we have done is to solve $3x = 15$.

   $x + 3 = 15$

   $x = $ ☐

Exercise 3, pages 11 - 12

4. Solve $x - 3 = 15$.

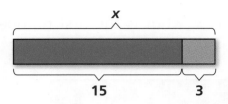

$x = $ ▢

5. Solve $y - 5 = 11$.

6. Solve $7 - x = 4$.

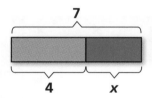

7. Solve $20 - y = 11$.

8. Solve $\frac{1}{3}x = 15$.

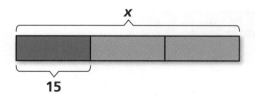

We also write $\frac{1}{3}x$ as $\frac{x}{3}$.

$\frac{1}{3}x = 15$

$x = $ ▢

9. Solve $\frac{1}{4}y = 3$.

16

Exercise 4, pages 13 - 14

1. Solve the equations.

   (a) $x + 1 = 4$

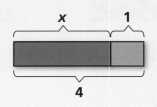

   (b) $k + 5 = 6$

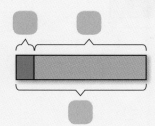

   (c) $2 + p = 5$

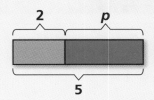

   (d) $4 + h = 9$

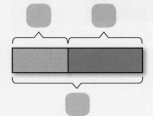

   (e) $m + 3 = 5$

   (f) $7 + y = 10$

2. Solve the equations.

   (a) $\frac{1}{4}x = 7$

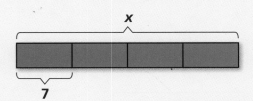

   (b) $\frac{k}{6} = 5$

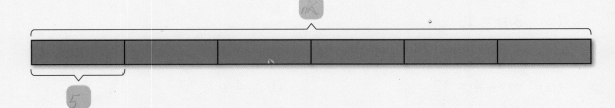

   (c) $\frac{1}{5}m = 3$

3. Solve the equation.

(a) $x - 1 = 4$

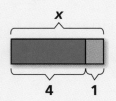

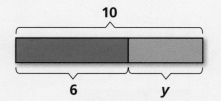

(b) $k - 5 = 6$

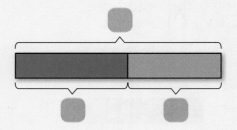

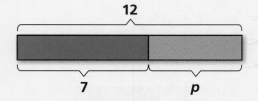

(c) $10 - y = 6$

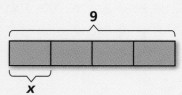

(d) $12 - p = 7$

(e) $m - 3 = 5$

(f) $9 - h = 1$

4. Solve the equation.

(a) $4x = 9$

(b) $5k = 20$

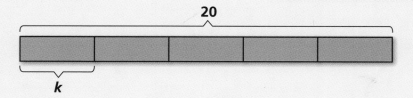

(c) $3m = 15$

5. Solve the equations.

(a) $m - 4 = 12$

(b) $4m = 12$

(c) $\frac{1}{4}m = 12$

(d) $\frac{m}{12} = 4$

(e) $m + 4 = 12$

(f) $12 - m = 4$

18

3 Algebraic Expressions II

There are x apples in a box and y oranges in a crate. Mrs. Thomas bought 3 boxes of apples and a crate of oranges. How many fruits did she buy? Express the answer in terms of x and y.

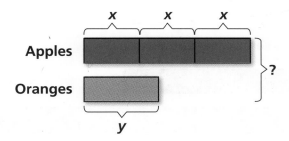

Number of apples bought   = $3x$
Number of oranges bought   = y
Total number of fruits bought = $3x + y$

Mrs. Thomas bought $(3x + y)$ fruits.

There are 20 apples in a box and 30 oranges in a crate. Mr. Johnson bought x boxes of apples and y boxes of oranges. How many fruits did he buy? Express the answer in terms of x and y.

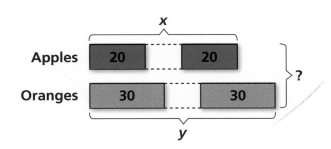

Number of apples bought   = $20x$
Number of oranges bought   = $30y$
Total number of fruits bought = $20x + 30y$

Mr. Johnson bought $(20x + 30y)$ fruits.

1. A telephone company charges x cents for local calls and y cents for long-distance calls. Mr. Morris makes a 5-minute local call and a 4-minute long-distance call.

   (a) How much does Mr. Morris have to pay? Express the answer in terms of x and y.

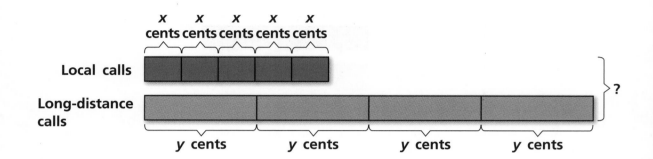

   Amount charged for local calls $= 5x$ cents

   Amount charged for long-distance calls $= 4y$ cents

   Mr. Morris has to pay $(5x + 4y)$ cents.

   (b) If $x = 10$ and $y = 30$, how much does Mr. Morris have to pay?

   $5x = \boxed{}$ cents

   $4y = \boxed{}$ cents

   $5x + 4y = \boxed{}$ cents

   Mr. Morris has to pay $\boxed{}$.

Exercise 5 & 6, pages 15 - 18

2. A small box contains 4 grapefruits and a big box contains 9 grapefruits.

   (a) Jimmy bought x small boxes and y big boxes of grapefruits. How many grapefruits did he buy? Express the answer in terms of x and y.

   Number of grapefruits in small boxes = ☐

   Number of grapefruits in big boxes = ☐

   Jimmy bought ☐ grapefruits.

   (b) If $x = 5$ and $y = 7$, how many grapefruits did Jimmy buy?

   Number of grapefruits in small boxes = ☐

   Number of grapefruits in big boxes = ☐

   Jimmy bought ☐ grapefruits.

3. A bus company charges its passengers the following rates for a single trip. Express the answers in terms of x, y and/or z.

Type of passengers	Fare for a single trip
Child	x cents
Adult	y cents
Senior Citizen	z cents

   (a) What is the bus fare for 2 adults?

   Bus fare for 2 adults = ☐ cents

   (b) What is the bus fare for 1 adult and 3 children?

   Bus fare for 3 children = ☐ cents

   Bus fare for 1 adult and 3 children = ☐ cents

   (c) What is the bus fare for 2 adults, 3 children and a senior citizen?

   Bus fare for 2 adults, 3 children and 1 senior citizen = ☐ cents

4. A postage company sells 27-cent, 42-cent and 59-cent stamps.
   Mr. Taylor buys x 27-cent, y 42-cent and z 59-cent stamps.

   (a) How much does Mr. Taylor have to pay for the stamps? Express
       the answers in terms of x, y and z.

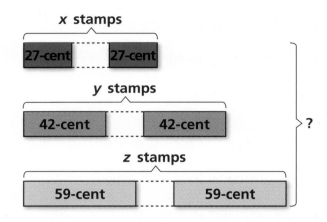

Cost of 27-cent stamps = ⬜ cents

Cost of 42-cent stamps = ⬜ cents

Cost of 59-cent stamps = ⬜ cents

Mr. Taylor has to pay ⬜ for the stamps.

   (b) If $x = 4$, $y = 5$ and $z = 3$, how much does Mr. Taylor have to pay
       for the stamps?

Cost of 27-cent stamps = ⬜ cents

Cost of 42-cent stamps = ⬜ cents

Cost of 59-cent stamps = ⬜ cents

Mr. Taylor has to pay ⬜ for the stamps.

Exercise 7, pages 19 - 20

1. There are x girls and y boys in a school. Each girl has 4 buttons on her skirt and each boy has 5 buttons on his shirt. What is the total number of buttons in terms of x and y?

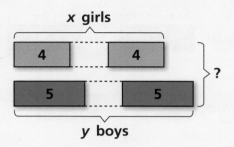

2. There are 360 fifth-graders and 440 sixth-graders in a school. Each fifth-grader has x books and each sixth-grader has y books. What is the total number of books in terms of x and y?

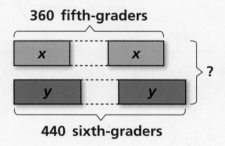

3. Larry bought x books, y files and z pens from a school supplies store. Each book cost $10, each file cost $5 and each pen cost $2. How much did the items cost in all? Express the answer in terms of x, y and z.

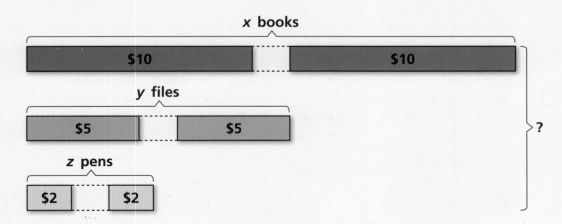

4. Mrs. Fernandez bought 40 notepads, 15 markers and 20 pencils from a school supplies store. Each notepad cost x, each marker cost y and each pencil cost z. How much did the items cost in all in terms of x, y and z?

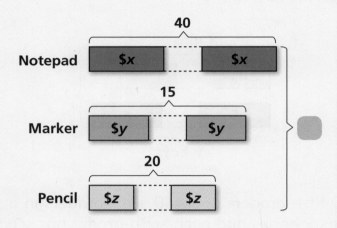

5. The table shows the cost of a movie ticket.

Type of patron	Price of ticket
Child	$x
Adult	$y
Senior Citizen	$z

(a) What is the total cost of movie tickets for 3 children? Express the answer in terms of x.

(b) What is the total cost of movie tickets for 2 adults, 3 children and 2 senior citizens? Express the answer in terms of x, y and z.

(c) If $x = 6$, $y = 10$ and $z = 5$, how much does Mrs. Brown have to pay for 2 adults, 3 children and 2 senior citizens?

6. At a farm, Ben and Kathy were each given a bucket that weighed x grams. Ben picked y grams of blueberries. The blueberries Kathy picked were 3 times as heavy as Ben's.

   (a) How heavy was Ben's bucket of blueberries in terms of x and y?

   (b) How heavy was Kathy's bucket of blueberries in terms of x and y?

   (c) Kathy picked 400 g more blueberries than Ben. Her bucket of blueberries weighed 900 g. How heavy was the bucket?

7. Zachary saved x nickels and y dimes last month. Lily saved x nickels and $2y$ dimes. Lily saved \$2 more than Zachary and the total number of her dimes is 4 times the total number of her nickels.

   (a) How many coins does Zachary have?

   (b) How much did Lily save?

   (c) How much did Zachary save?

8. The table shows the number of children in two groups.

	Green group	Yellow group	Total
Boys	x	$2x$	
Girls	y	z	
Total	13		

   (a) Complete the table.

   (b) Given that there are 6 girls in green group, write an **algebraic equation** in terms of x. Use the equation to find the number of boys in the yellow group.

   (c) Write an expression to show the difference between the total number of boys and the total number of girls.

4 Graphs of Functions

Dylan is 3 years older than Ellen. When Ellen was 1 year old, how old was Dylan?

When Ellen was 1 year old, Dylan was 4 years old.
When Ellen was 2 years old, Dylan was 5 years old.
When Ellen is x years old, Dylan is $(x + 3)$ years old.
How old will Dylan be when Ellen is 34 years old?

Ellen's age	Dylan's age
x	$x + 3$
1	$1 + 3 = 4$
2	$2 + 3 = 5$
3	$3 + 3 = 6$

Based on the table, we can draw a **graph**.

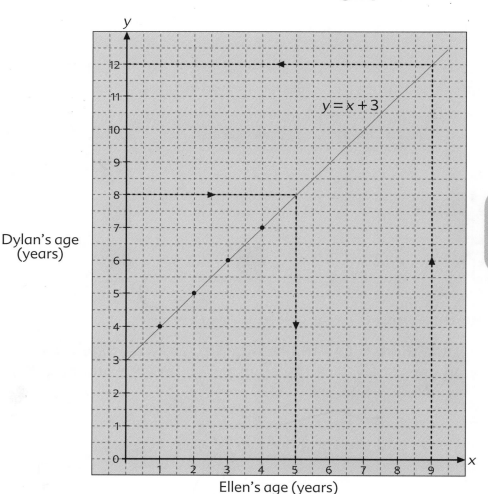

Dylan's age (years)

Ellen's age (years)

$y = x + 3$

We indicate the points on a graph. Then we join all the points.

26

Look at the graph on pg 26. Find the value of $x + 3$ when $x = 9$.

When $x = 9$, $x + 3 = \boxed{}$.

From the graph, find the value of x when

$x + 3 = 8$,
$x + 3 = 10$.

This means we know that when Ellen is 9 years old,

Dylan is $\boxed{}$ years old.

1. Study the graph.

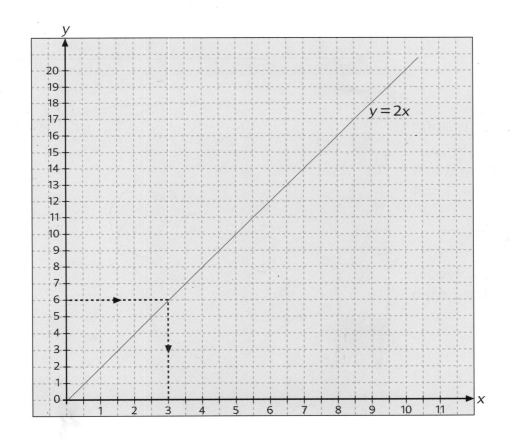

Use the graph to solve for x.
(a) $2x = 6$
(b) $2x = 10$
(c) $2x = 7$
(d) $2x = 0$

Exercise 8, pages 21 - 24

2. (a) Use the graph to solve for x.
   (i) $3x - 2 = 4$
   (ii) $3x - 2 = 5$
   (iii) $3x - 2 = 6$

   (b) What are the possible values for k if the solution to $3x - 2 = k$ is an **integer**?

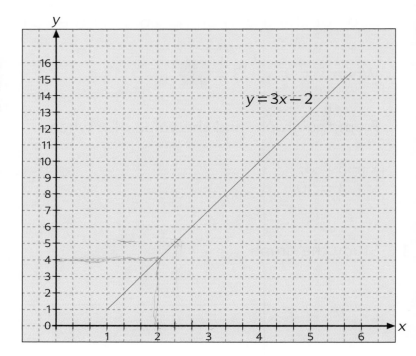

3. (a) Use the graph to solve for x.
   (i) $2x - 1 = 9$
   (ii) $2x - 1 = 4$

   (b) Write an equation that can be solved using the graph.

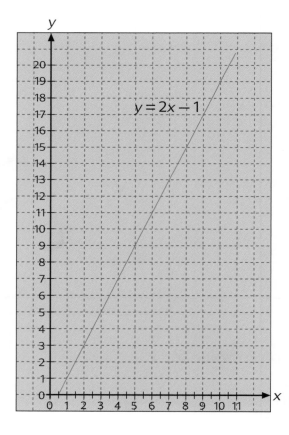

Exercise 9, pages 25 - 28

1. Use the graph to solve for x.

   (a) $x + 4 = 10$
   (b) $x + 4 = 4$

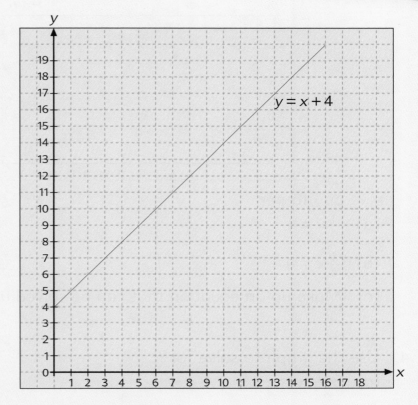

2. Use the graph to solve for x.

   (a) $3x + 1 = 19$
   (b) $3x + 1 = 10$
   (c) $3x + 1 = 1$

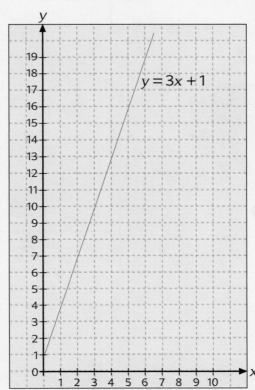

3. Use the graph to solve for x.

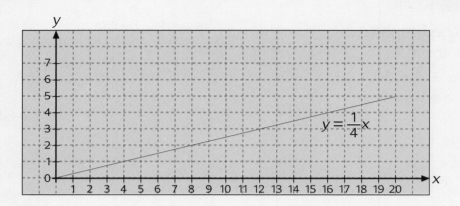

(a) $\frac{1}{4}x = 1$

(b) $\frac{1}{4}x = 4$

(c) Make up an equation that can be solved using the graph.

4. Use the graph to solve for x.

(a) $3 - x = 2$

(b) $3 - x = \frac{1}{2}$

(c) $4 - x = 2$

Use the solution to $3 - x = 2$ to solve $4 - x = 2$.

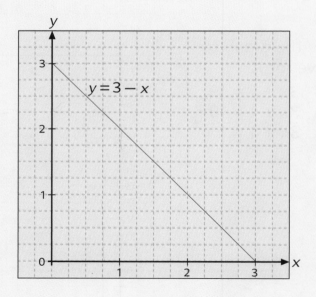

REVIEW 1

1. (a) Find the value of $4p$ when $p = 2.5$.
    (b) Solve $4p = 10$.

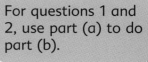 

For questions 1 and 2, use part (a) to do part (b).

2. (a) Find the value of $3s - 1$ when $s = 4$.
    (b) Solve $3s - 1 = 11$.

3. (a) The perimeter of an isosceles triangle is x inches. The lengths of two of the sides are 3 inches each. Find an expression, in terms of x, for the length of the third side.
    (b) The perimeter of a rectangle is y centimeters. Its length is 7 centimeters. Find an expression, in terms of y, for the width.

4. The length of a rectangle is 4 times its width.
    (a) Given that the width is a centimeters, find an expression for its perimeter in terms of a.
    (b) Given that the length is b centimeters, find an expression for its perimeter in terms of b.

5. Billy arranges consecutive whole numbers 1 through 5 such that they add up to the same number horizontally and vertically. Billy does the same thing for numbers 2 through 6. He records the results in the table on page 32.

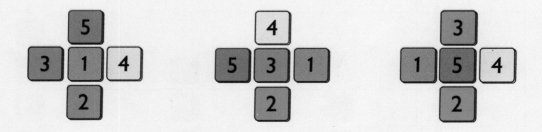

Numbers on tiles	Sum of numbers horizontally	Sum of numbers vertically	Number in the middle
1 to 5	8 9 10	8 9 10	1 3 5
2 to 6	11 12 13	11 12 13	2 4 6
3 to 7		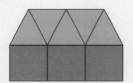	

When the smallest number used is x, write an expression, in terms of x,

(a) for the other four numbers used.
(b) for the numbers in the middle.
(c) for the sums of the numbers horizontally and vertically.

6. Trina used attribute blocks to make a pattern.

Pattern 1   Pattern 2   Pattern 3

Complete the table.

Pattern	Number of square pieces	Number of triangle pieces	Total number of pieces
1	1	1	2
2	2	3	
3	3		
4			
5			
6			
7			

7. The graph shows how the length of one side, y, of a rectangle is related to the length of the other side, x.

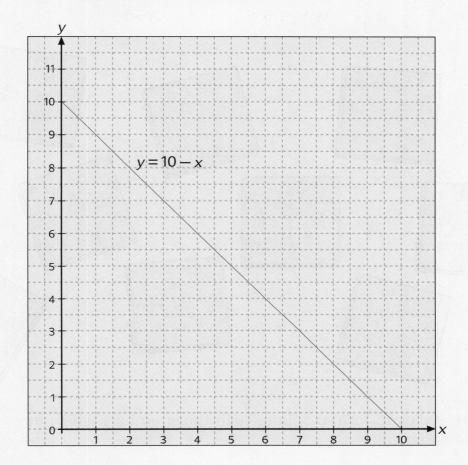

$y = 10 - x$

(a) Use the graph to solve $10 - x = 4$. Explain the meaning of the solution.

(b) Use the graph to find the length of the other side when one of the rectangle's sides is 7 cm.

(c) The rectangle has a perimeter of 20 cm. Find the length of its sides for its area to be greatest possible.

Review 1, pages 29 - 32

2 FRACTIONS AND DECIMALS

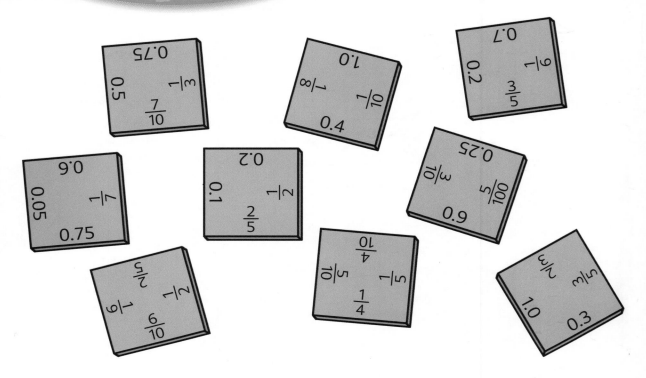

Piece the 9 tiles to form a square such that numbers which are side by side have the same value.

This is possible.

| 1/2 | 5/10 |

This is not possible.

| 1/2 | 3/4 |

1 Fractions and Decimals

Write a **fraction** as a **decimal**.

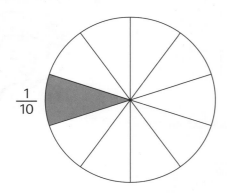

$\frac{1}{10}$

This is **1 tenth**.

It is also written as **0.1**.

$\frac{1}{10} = 0.1$

1. Write each fraction as a decimal.

(a)

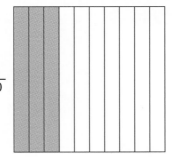

$\frac{3}{10}$

This is 3 **tenths**.

It is also written as ⬜.

$\frac{3}{10} =$ ⬜

(b)

$\frac{1}{2}$ → $\frac{5}{10}$

This is ⬜ tenths.

It is also written as ⬜.

$\frac{1}{2} =$ ⬜

(c)

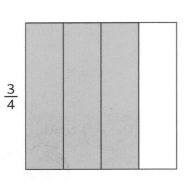

$\frac{3}{4}$

This is **75 hundredths**.

It is also written as **0.75**.

$\frac{3}{4}$ =

(d)

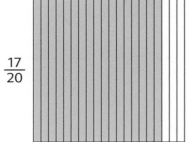

$\frac{17}{20}$

This is **hundredths**.

It is also written as .

$\frac{17}{20}$ =

2. Write each fraction as a decimal.

(a) $\frac{1}{2} = 1 \div 2$

   =

$2\overline{)1.0}$

(b) $\frac{3}{4} = 3 \div 4$

   =

$4\overline{)3.0}$

(c) $\frac{17}{20} = 17 \div 20$

   =

$20\overline{)1\,7}$

Exercise 1, pages 33 - 34

Write a decimal as a fraction. **Express** the answer in the simplest form.

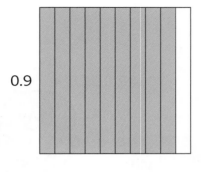

0.9

$$0.9 = \frac{9}{10}$$

This is **0.9**.

It is also written as $\frac{9}{10}$.

0.4

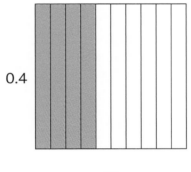

$\frac{2}{5}$

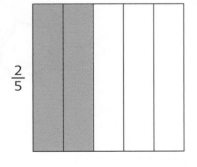

This is **0.4**.

It is also written as $\frac{4}{10}$.

$\frac{4}{10}$ is equal to $\frac{2}{5}$.

$$0.4 = \frac{4}{10}$$
$$= \frac{2}{5}$$

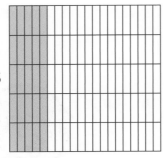

0.25

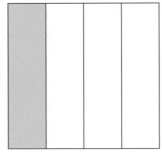

$\frac{1}{4}$

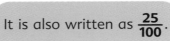
This is **0.25**.

It is also written as $\frac{25}{100}$.

$\frac{25}{100}$ is equal to $\frac{1}{4}$.

$$0.25 = \frac{25}{100}$$
$$= \frac{1}{4}$$

3. Express as decimals.

(a) $\frac{7}{10}$ =

(b) $\frac{97}{100}$ =

(c) $\frac{47}{50}$ =

(d) $1\frac{2}{5}$ =

(e) $2\frac{1}{4}$ =

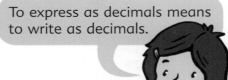
To express as decimals means to write as decimals.

4. Express as fractions.

(a) 0.1 =

(b) 0.3 =

(c) 0.5 =

(d) 0.6 =

(e) 0.49 =

(f) 1.07 =

(g) 1.98 =

To express as fractions means to write as fractions.

Exercise 2, pages 35 - 36

2 Negative Fractions and Decimals

A dam has sprung a leak.

Each time the water level in the dam is measured, it has fallen by $\frac{1}{2}$ m.

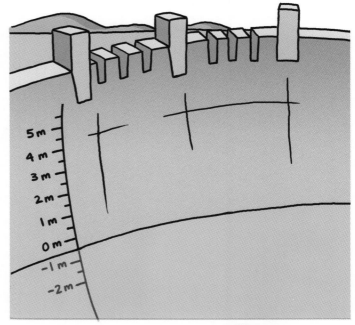

$3 \text{ m} - \frac{1}{2} \text{ m} = 2\frac{1}{2} \text{ m}$

$2\frac{1}{2} \text{ m} - \frac{1}{2} \text{ m} = 2 \text{ m}$

$2 \text{ m} - \frac{1}{2} \text{ m} = 1\frac{1}{2} \text{ m}$

$1\frac{1}{2} \text{ m} - \frac{1}{2} \text{ m} = 1 \text{ m}$

$1 \text{ m} - \frac{1}{2} \text{ m} = \frac{1}{2} \text{ m}$

$\frac{1}{2} \text{ m} - \frac{1}{2} \text{ m} = 0 \text{ m}$

$0 \text{ m} - \frac{1}{2} \text{ m} = \boxed{} \text{ m}$

What is the water level now?

When the water level is $\frac{1}{2}$ m below the zero mark, we say that the the water level is at **negative** one half meter.
We write it like this:

Numbers less than 0 are negative numbers.

The water level is $-\frac{1}{2}$ m.

$-\frac{1}{2}$ is less than 0.

Is $-\frac{1}{2}$ less than $\frac{1}{4}$?

1. Ariel draws a **vertical number line**. She writes some numbers on it.

She writes the following:

$\frac{1}{5}$ at H,

$1\frac{2}{5}$ at C,

$-\frac{1}{5}$ at I,

$-1\frac{4}{5}$ at P.

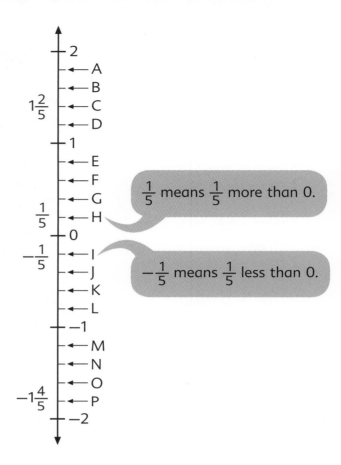

$\frac{1}{5}$ means $\frac{1}{5}$ more than 0.

$-\frac{1}{5}$ means $\frac{1}{5}$ less than 0.

(a) At what point should Ariel write each of these numbers?

(i) $\frac{2}{5}$ (ii) $-\frac{3}{5}$

(iii) $\frac{4}{5}$ (iv) $-1\frac{3}{5}$

(b) Using the numbers on the number line, complete the sentences.

(i) ▢ is greater than ▢.

(ii) ▢ is smaller than ▢.

$-\frac{1}{5}$ is greater than $-1\frac{4}{5}$.

-1 is less than $-\frac{1}{5}$.

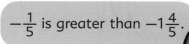

Exercise 3, pages 37 - 38

2. Billy writes some numbers on the number line.

He writes the following:

0.4 at G,

1.8 at A,

−0.2 at I,

−1.8 at P.

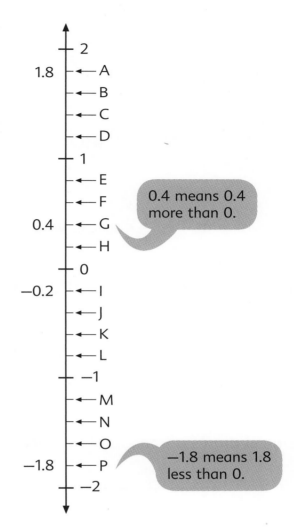

(a) At what point should Billy write each of these numbers?
   (i)   0.8   (ii) −0.8
   (iii) 1.6   (iv) −1.6

(b) Using the numbers on the number line, complete the sentences.

   (i)   [ ] is greater than [ ].

   (ii) [ ] is smaller than [ ].

3. Cassandra draws a **horizontal number line**.

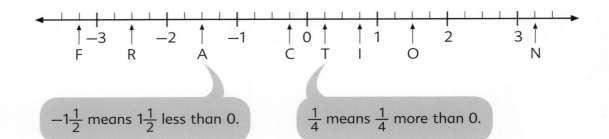

−1$\frac{1}{2}$ means 1$\frac{1}{2}$ less than 0.

$\frac{1}{4}$ means $\frac{1}{4}$ more than 0.

The value at T is $\frac{1}{4}$ and the value at A is −1$\frac{1}{2}$.

What is the value at each of the following points?

(a) F   (b) R

(c) C   (d) I

(e) O   (f) N

4. Daniel draws a horizontal number line.

What is the value at points A, B, C and D when the value of

(a) x is 0,

(b) x is 2,

(c) x is −1,

(d) x is −5.

Exercise 4, pages 39 - 40

3 Comparing Numbers

Which number is greater, $\frac{1}{4}$ or $-\frac{1}{2}$?

Subtract $\frac{1}{2}$ from 0 to get $-\frac{1}{2}$.

Add $\frac{1}{4}$ to 0 to get $\frac{1}{4}$.

$\frac{1}{4}$ is greater than $-\frac{1}{2}$.

$$\frac{1}{4} > -\frac{1}{2}$$

Which is smaller, $-\frac{1}{4}$ or $-\frac{1}{2}$?

Subtract $\frac{1}{4}$ from 0 to get $-\frac{1}{4}$.

Subtract more from 0 to get $-\frac{1}{2}$.

$-\frac{1}{2}$ is smaller than $-\frac{1}{4}$.

$$-\frac{1}{2} < -\frac{1}{4}$$

1. Which number is greater, $-\frac{3}{8}$ or $-\frac{5}{8}$?

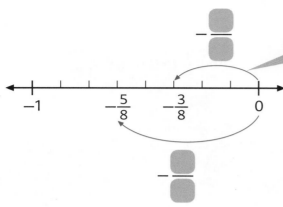

Subtract ⬜ from 0 to get $-\frac{3}{8}$.

Do we subtract more or less from 0 to get $-\frac{5}{8}$?

 is greater than ⬜.

⬜ > ⬜

2. Which number is smaller, $-1\frac{3}{4}$ or $-1\frac{2}{3}$?

$-1\frac{3}{4} = -1\frac{9}{12}$

$-1\frac{2}{3} = -1\frac{8}{12}$

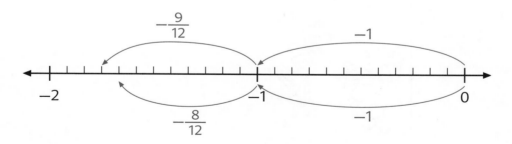

 is smaller than ⬜.

⬜ < ⬜

44

Exercise 5, pages 41 - 42

3. Which number is smaller, $-\frac{1}{2}$ or -0.2?

Method 1:

$-\frac{1}{2} = $

Write $-\frac{1}{2}$ as a decimal.

☐ is smaller than ☐ .

☐ < ☐

Method 2:

$$-\frac{8}{10} \quad -\frac{7}{10} \quad -\frac{6}{10} \quad -\frac{5}{10} \quad -\frac{4}{10} \quad -\frac{3}{10} \quad -\frac{2}{10} \quad -\frac{1}{10} \qquad \frac{1}{10} \quad \frac{2}{10} \quad \frac{3}{10} \quad \frac{4}{10} \quad \frac{5}{10} \quad \frac{6}{10} \quad \frac{7}{10} \quad \frac{8}{10}$$

$$-0.8 \; -0.7 \; -0.6 \; -0.5 \; -0.4 \; -0.3 \; -0.2 \; -0.1 \quad 0 \quad 0.1 \quad 0.2 \quad 0.3 \quad 0.4 \quad 0.5 \quad 0.6 \quad 0.7 \quad 0.8$$

$-0.2 = -\dfrac{\boxed{}}{10}$

$-\frac{1}{2} = -\dfrac{\boxed{}}{10}$

Write -0.2 as a fraction.

☐ is smaller than ☐ .

☐ < ☐

4. Explain why $-\frac{3}{4}$ is smaller than -0.34.

Exercise 6, pages 43 - 44

1. Which number is smaller?

   (a) $\frac{1}{2}$ or $-\frac{3}{4}$ (b) $\frac{1}{2}$ or $-2\frac{4}{5}$ (c) -0.5 or -0.1

   (d) -0.25 or $\frac{3}{4}$ (e) $-\frac{2}{5}$ or $-\frac{3}{5}$ (f) $-3\frac{1}{7}$ or $-3\frac{3}{7}$

   (g) -0.9 or -0.2 (h) -0.05 or -0.5 (i) $\frac{1}{4}$ or 0.4

2. Which number is greater?

   (a) $-\frac{1}{3}$ or $-\frac{1}{4}$ (b) $-\frac{3}{4}$ or $-\frac{3}{8}$ (c) $1\frac{3}{7}$ or $-2\frac{3}{5}$

   (d) $-2\frac{4}{7}$ or $-2\frac{4}{9}$ (e) $-\frac{3}{4}$ or $-\frac{2}{3}$ (f) $-\frac{2}{5}$ or $-\frac{1}{2}$

   (g) -0.4 or $-\frac{4}{5}$ (h) -1.2 or $-1\frac{3}{8}$ (i) 2.07 or $-2\frac{7}{10}$

3. Use $<$, $>$ or $=$ in each ⬤ to make a correct statement.

   (a) 0.1 ⬤ $-\frac{2}{3}$ (b) 0.7 ⬤ $-\frac{1}{2}$

   (c) $-1\frac{3}{4}$ ⬤ -1.7 (d) $-2\frac{4}{5}$ ⬤ -2.8

4. Arrange the numbers from the smallest to the greatest.

   (a) 0, 3, -0.4, -0.5 (b) 0, 2, $\frac{1}{4}$, $-\frac{1}{4}$

   (c) $-\frac{3}{4}$, $-\frac{3}{5}$, $-\frac{4}{5}$ (d) $-\frac{3}{4}$, $-\frac{5}{6}$, $-\frac{7}{8}$

5. Arrange the numbers in descending order.

   (a) -1.3, $-1\frac{3}{5}$, $-1\frac{3}{4}$ (b) -3.15, $-3\frac{1}{5}$, $-3\frac{2}{5}$

   (c) $-\frac{19}{20}$, $-\frac{9}{10}$, -0.19 (d) -0.55, $-\frac{7}{5}$, $-\frac{3}{4}$

6. (a) Arrange the digits 3, 4 and 5 in the form 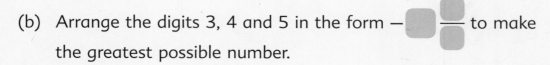 to make the greatest possible number.

   (b) Arrange the digits 3, 4 and 5 in the form $-$ ▢$\frac{▢}{▢}$ to make the greatest possible number.

7. Name a number between -1.3 and -1.4.

3 THE FOUR OPERATIONS OF FRACTIONS

a, e, i, o and u are vowels.

The other letters of the alphabet are consonants.

3 out of 5 of the letters in my name are vowels.

$\frac{3}{5}$ of the letters are vowels.

MARIA

2 out of 4 of the letters in my name are vowels.

$\frac{2}{4}$ or $\frac{1}{2}$ of the letters in my name are vowels.

JAKE

$\frac{2}{3}$ of the letters in the name of this state are vowels. What is this state?

Use other fractions.

1 Addition and Subtraction of Fractions

Davio ate $\frac{1}{4}$ of a pizza. Ethan ate $\frac{1}{3}$ of the same pizza.

What fraction of the pizza did they eat altogether?

Davio

Ethan

$$\frac{1}{4} + \frac{1}{3} = \boxed{}$$

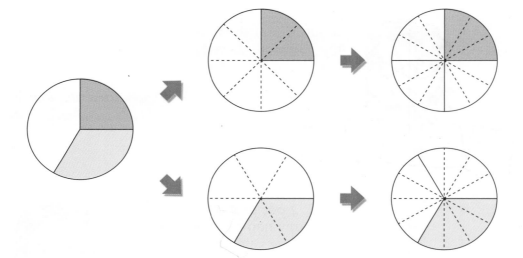

$$\frac{1}{4} = \frac{2}{8} = \frac{3}{12}$$

$$\frac{1}{3} = \frac{2}{6} = \frac{3}{9} = \frac{4}{12}$$

12 is a **multiple** of 4.
12 is also a multiple of 3.

So, $\frac{1}{4} + \frac{1}{3} = \dfrac{\boxed{}}{12} + \dfrac{\boxed{}}{12}$

$$= \dfrac{\boxed{}}{12}.$$

They ate of the pizza altogether.

48

1. There were some students in a summer class. $\frac{2}{3}$ of the students went to the museum. $\frac{1}{4}$ of the students went to the zoo. The rest of them remained in the school. What fraction of the students went for a class trip?

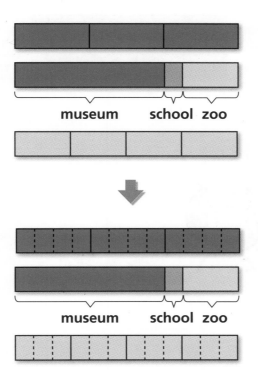

$\frac{2}{3} = \frac{4}{6} = \frac{6}{9} = \frac{8}{12}$

$\frac{1}{4} = \frac{2}{8} = \frac{3}{12}$

12 is a **common multiple** of 3 and 4.

So, $\frac{2}{3} + \frac{1}{4} = \frac{\boxed{}}{12} + \frac{\boxed{}}{12}$

$= \frac{\boxed{}}{12}$.

 of the students went for a class trip.

2. Christine has $\frac{4}{5}$ m of red ribbon. She needs a blue ribbon that is $\frac{1}{2}$ m longer than the red ribbon. Find the length of the blue ribbon.

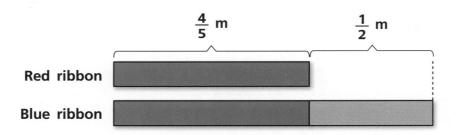

Method 1:

10 is a common multiple of 5 and 2.

$$\frac{4}{5} = \frac{8}{10}$$

$$\frac{1}{2} = \frac{2}{4} = \frac{3}{6} = \frac{4}{8} = \frac{5}{10}$$

$$\frac{4}{5} + \frac{1}{2} = \frac{\square}{10} + \frac{\square}{10}$$

$$= \frac{\square}{10}$$

$$= 1\frac{\square}{10}$$

The blue ribbon is ▢ m long.

Method 2:

$$\frac{4}{5} = \frac{8}{10} = \frac{12}{15} = \frac{16}{20}$$

$$\frac{1}{2} = \frac{5}{10} = \frac{10}{20}$$

$$\frac{4}{5} + \frac{1}{2} = \frac{\square}{20} + \frac{\square}{20}$$

$$= \frac{\square}{20}$$

$$= 1\frac{\square}{20}$$

$$= 1\frac{\square}{10}$$

20 is also a common multiple of 5 and 2.

But 10 is the **least common multiple** of 5 and 2.

The blue ribbon is ▢ m long.

3. Mary has a blue ribbon that is $1\frac{2}{3}$ m long. She has a red ribbon that is $1\frac{3}{5}$ m long.

   (a) How much longer is the blue ribbon than the red ribbon?
   (b) What is the total length of the 2 ribbons?

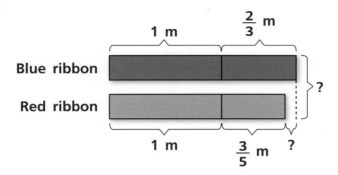

(a) **Method 1:**

$$1\frac{2}{3} = 1\frac{4}{6} = 1\frac{6}{9} = 1\frac{8}{12} = 1\frac{10}{15}$$

$$1\frac{3}{5} = 1\frac{6}{10} = 1\frac{9}{15}$$

$$1\frac{2}{3} - 1\frac{3}{5} = 1\frac{\boxed{}}{15} - 1\frac{\boxed{}}{15} = \frac{\boxed{}}{15}$$

> Why do we stop when the **denominator** is 15?

The blue ribbon is $\frac{\boxed{}}{15}$ m longer than the red ribbon.

Method 2:

$$1\frac{2}{3} = 1\frac{4}{6} = 1\frac{6}{9} = 1\frac{8}{12} = 1\frac{10}{15} = \ldots = 1\frac{\boxed{}}{30}$$

$$1\frac{3}{5} = 1\frac{6}{10} = 1\frac{9}{15} = 1\frac{12}{20} = 1\frac{15}{25} = 1\frac{\boxed{}}{30}$$

$$1\frac{2}{3} - 1\frac{3}{5} = 1\frac{\boxed{}}{30} - 1\frac{\boxed{}}{30}$$

$$= \frac{\boxed{}}{30}$$

$$= \frac{\boxed{}}{15}$$

> 15 is the least common multiple of 3 and 5. 30 is also a common multiple of 3 and 5.

The blue ribbon is $\frac{\boxed{}}{15}$ m longer than the red ribbon.

(b) $1\frac{2}{3} = 1\frac{4}{6} = 1\frac{6}{9} = 1\frac{8}{12} = 1\frac{\square}{15}$

Add the whole numbers.
Add the fractions.

$1\frac{2}{5} = 1\frac{4}{10} = 1\frac{\square}{15}$

$1\frac{2}{3} + 1\frac{3}{5} = 1\frac{\square}{15} + 1\frac{\square}{15}$

$= \square$

The two ribbons are $\square$ m long.

4. Mrs. Ding baked a cake. She gave $\frac{1}{2}$ of it to her sister. She also gave $\frac{1}{3}$ of the cake to her neighbor. Find the fraction of the cake that she gave away.

6 is the least common multiple of 2 and 3.

5. The length of a rectangle is $\frac{1}{10}$ ft longer than its width. The length is $\frac{2}{3}$ ft. Find the width of the rectangle.

What is the common multiple that you should use?

6. Add or subtract. State how you found the least common multiple.

(a) $\frac{1}{4} + \frac{1}{3}$

(b) $\frac{2}{3} + \frac{1}{4}$

(c) $\frac{4}{5} + \frac{1}{2}$

(d) $\frac{2}{3} - \frac{3}{5}$

(e) $\frac{2}{3} + \frac{3}{5}$

(f) $\frac{1}{2} + \frac{1}{3}$

(g) $\frac{2}{3} - \frac{1}{10}$

(h) $4\frac{2}{3} - 1\frac{1}{4}$

(i) $3\frac{1}{2} + 2\frac{1}{5}$

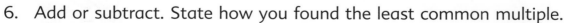

Exercise 1, pages 45 - 46

7. At a fair, $\frac{3}{8}$ of the visitors are boys, $\frac{1}{3}$ are girls, $\frac{1}{8}$ are men and the rest are women.

(a) What fraction of the visitors are children?

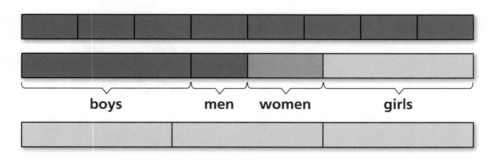

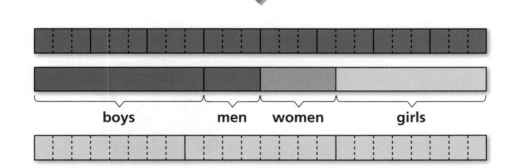

$$\frac{3}{8} + \frac{1}{3} = \frac{\boxed{}}{\boxed{}} + \frac{\boxed{}}{\boxed{}}$$

$$= \frac{\boxed{}}{\boxed{}}$$

What is the least common multiple of 3 and 8?

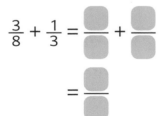

 $\frac{\boxed{}}{\boxed{}}$ of the visitors are children.

(b) What fraction of the visitors are female?

What fraction of the visitors are women?
What fraction of the visitors are girls?

8. $\frac{1}{6}$ of a group of people are children and $\frac{1}{10}$ are boys. What fraction of the group of people are girls?

is the least common multiple of 6 and 10.

Is it 60?

9. Edna's sister is $\frac{3}{4}$ m tall. Edna is $\frac{3}{10}$ m taller than her sister. Find Edna's height.

What is the least common multiple that you should use?

Is it 40?

10. Fariz and Gerrie each have a container with $\frac{3}{4}$ ℓ of water. Fariz adds $\frac{5}{6}$ ℓ of water to his container. Gerrie adds $\frac{3}{8}$ ℓ of water to his container.
(a) Who has more water now?
(b) How much more?

What is the least common multiple that you should use?

11. Add. Write each answer in its simplest form.

(a) $\frac{1}{3} + \frac{1}{5}$

(b) $\frac{1}{4} + \frac{2}{3}$

(c) $\frac{3}{4} + \frac{3}{5}$

(d) $\frac{1}{6} + \frac{3}{10}$

(e) $\frac{2}{3} + \frac{5}{6}$

What is the common multiple we should use?

For $\frac{1}{3} + \frac{1}{5}$, I use 15.

Write a word problem that can be solved by doing the above addition.

12. Subtract. Write each answer in its simplest form.

(a) $\frac{1}{2} - \frac{2}{5}$

(b) $\frac{5}{6} - \frac{3}{4}$

(c) $\frac{7}{10} - \frac{5}{6}$

Write a word problem that can be solved by doing the above subtraction.

Gilbert used $\frac{3}{4}$ ℓ of concentrated lemon syrup and $\frac{a}{3}$ ℓ of water to make lemonade. Find how much lemonade he made in terms of a.

$$\frac{3}{4} = \frac{6}{8} = \frac{9}{12}$$

$$\frac{a}{3} = \frac{2a}{6} = \frac{3a}{9} = \frac{4a}{12}$$

$$\frac{9}{12} + \frac{4a}{12} = \frac{9 + 4a}{12}$$

Is it possible that Gilbert used more than 1 ℓ of water?

What if $a = 1$?

What if $a = 6$?

He made $\frac{9 + 4a}{12}$ ℓ of lemonade.

13. Find the missing **algebraic expression**.

$$\frac{x}{2} + \frac{1}{6} = \frac{\boxed{}}{6}$$

14. Find the missing algebraic expression.

(a) $\frac{1}{2} + \frac{y}{5} = \frac{\boxed{}}{10}$

(b) What is the value of $\frac{1}{2} + \frac{y}{5}$ when

   (i) $y = 1$

   (ii) $y = 2$

15. Box A weighs $3\frac{4}{5}$ kg. Box B weighs $4\frac{1}{2}$ kg.
    Find the total weight of the two boxes.

16. Jon is $5\frac{2}{3}$ ft tall. Jon is $\frac{1}{2}$ ft shorter than Kyle. Find Kyle's height.

17. Mrs. Smith baked a 3-lb cake and gave Carla $\frac{1}{3}$ of it. Miss Li baked a 4-lb cake and gave Carla $\frac{1}{4}$ of it. Carla says she now has $\frac{7}{12}$ of a cake because $\frac{1}{3} + \frac{1}{4} = \frac{7}{12}$. Do you agree with Carla? Explain your answer.

Exercise 2, pages 47 – 49

1. Find the value.

   (a) $\frac{1}{12} + \frac{5}{12}$

   (b) $3\frac{2}{3} - 1\frac{1}{3}$

   (c) $2\frac{3}{4} + \frac{2}{3}$

   (d) $\frac{3}{4} - \frac{1}{4}$

   (e) $4\frac{3}{8} + 1\frac{1}{8}$

   (f) $\frac{3}{5} + \frac{4}{5}$

   (g) $\frac{1}{2} + \frac{1}{3}$

   (h) $2\frac{2}{3} - 1\frac{1}{6}$

   (i) $3\frac{3}{5} - 1\frac{7}{8}$

2. Felix ate $2\frac{1}{4}$ pies. Josie ate $1\frac{1}{3}$ pies. How many pies did they eat altogether?

3. $\frac{3}{5}$ of a group of visitors are children. $\frac{1}{3}$ of the group of visitors are boys. What fraction of the group of visitors are girls?

4. Two months ago, Josie was $\frac{2}{3}$ m tall. Now, she is $\frac{1}{6}$ m taller. Find Josie's height now.

5. Felicia has $3\frac{1}{2}$ kg of flour. Susie has $1\frac{5}{8}$ kg less flour than Felicia. Find the total amount of flour they have.

6. Mrs. Garner baked some muffins. She sold $\frac{3}{4}$ of the muffins on the first day. She sold $\frac{1}{6}$ more on the second day. She brought the rest home. What fraction of the muffins did Mrs. Garner bring home?

7. $\frac{1}{\triangle} + \frac{1}{\star} = \frac{7}{12}$

   What are the possible values of $\triangle$ and $\star$?

2 Multiplication and Division of Fractions

Davio ate $\frac{1}{4}$ of a pizza. Ethan ate $\frac{1}{3}$ of the **remaining** pizza. What is the fraction of the pizza that Ethan ate?

$1 - \frac{1}{4} = \frac{3}{4}$

First we find the amount of pizza remaining.

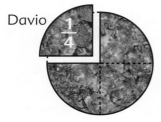
Davio

Ethan

$\frac{1}{3}$ of $\frac{3}{4}$ of the pizza is the same as $\frac{1}{4}$ of the whole pizza.

$\frac{1}{3} \times \frac{3}{4} = \frac{1}{4}$

Ethan ate $\frac{1}{4}$ of the pizza.

1. $\frac{2}{3}$ of the students in a class went to the museum. $\frac{1}{2}$ of the remaining students went to the zoo. The rest of them remained in the school. What fraction of the students remained in the school?

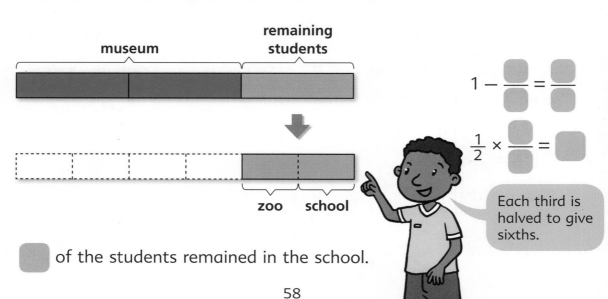

remaining
museum   students

zoo   school

$1 - \frac{\square}{\square} = \frac{\square}{\square}$

$\frac{1}{2} \times \frac{\square}{\square} = \square$

Each third is halved to give sixths.

☐ of the students remained in the school.

58

Amanda's house is $3\frac{3}{4}$ mi from her school. She walked $\frac{1}{3}$ of the distance. Find the distance she walked.

Method 1:

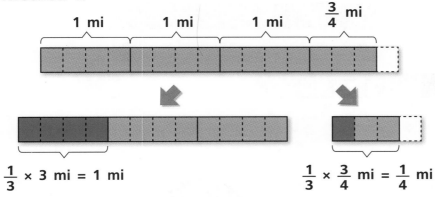

$\frac{1}{3} \times 3$ mi = 1 mi

$\frac{1}{3} \times \frac{3}{4}$ mi = $\frac{1}{4}$ mi

$\frac{1}{3} \times 3\frac{3}{4} = 1\frac{1}{4}$

$\frac{1}{3}$ of 3 is 1.

$\frac{1}{3}$ of $\frac{3}{4}$ is $\frac{1}{4}$.

So, $\frac{1}{3}$ of $3\frac{3}{4}$ is $1\frac{1}{4}$.

Amanda walked $1\frac{1}{4}$ miles.

Method 2:

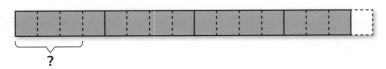

?

$3\frac{3}{4} = 15$ quarters

15 quarters $= \frac{15}{4}$

$\frac{1}{3} \times 3\frac{3}{4} = \frac{1}{3} \times 15$ quarters

$= 5$ quarters

$= 1\frac{1}{4}$

5 quarters $= \frac{5}{4}$

Amanda walked $1\frac{1}{4}$ miles.

2. Jim's bag weighs $4\frac{4}{5}$ kg. Madison's bag weighs $\frac{1}{4}$ that of Jim's. What is the weight of Madison's bag?

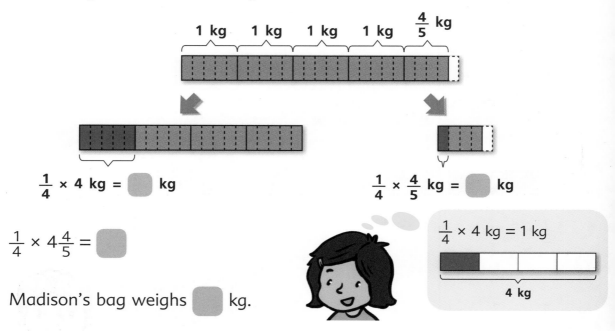

$$\frac{1}{4} \times 4 \text{ kg} = \boxed{} \text{ kg} \qquad\qquad \frac{1}{4} \times \frac{4}{5} \text{ kg} = \boxed{} \text{ kg}$$

$$\frac{1}{4} \times 4\frac{4}{5} = \boxed{}$$

Madison's bag weighs $\boxed{}$ kg.

$\frac{1}{4} \times 4$ kg = 1 kg

4 kg

3. There are $3\frac{1}{2}$ pies left over from a party. Ali takes $\frac{3}{4}$ of them home. How many pies does Ali take?

Method 1:

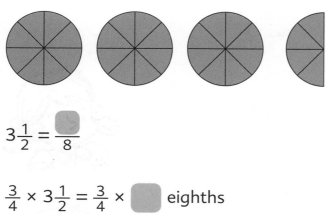

$$3\frac{1}{2} = \frac{\boxed{}}{8}$$

$$\frac{3}{4} \times 3\frac{1}{2} = \frac{3}{4} \times \boxed{} \text{ eighths}$$

$$= \boxed{}$$

Ali takes $\boxed{}$ pies.

Method 2:

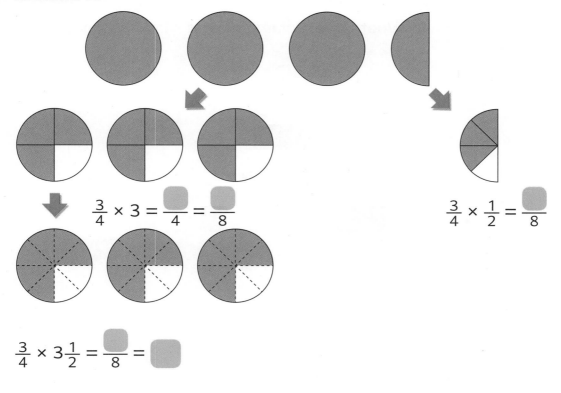

$$\frac{3}{4} \times 3 = \frac{\boxed{}}{4} = \frac{\boxed{}}{8}$$

$$\frac{3}{4} \times \frac{1}{2} = \frac{\boxed{}}{8}$$

$$\frac{3}{4} \times 3\frac{1}{2} = \frac{\boxed{}}{8} = \boxed{}$$

Ali takes $\boxed{}$ pies.

4. Emma bought $2\frac{1}{4}$ oz of spices. Cody bought $\frac{1}{2}$ the amount of spices Emma bought. How many oz of spices did Cody buy?

5. The longest side of a triangle is $2\frac{3}{4}$ times as long as the shortest side. The shortest side is $\frac{2}{3}$ in. Find the length of the longest side.

6. Multiply.

   (a) $\frac{1}{5} \times 10\frac{5}{7}$

   (b) $\frac{2}{3} \times 6\frac{4}{5}$

   (c) $\frac{5}{6} \times 11\frac{7}{8}$

Exercise 3, pages 50 – 51

Miss Terry has $\frac{2}{5}$ ℓ of acid in a beaker. She needs $1\frac{1}{2}$ times this volume for an experiment. What is the volume of acid Miss Terry needs for the experiment?

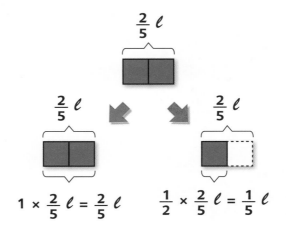

$1 \times \frac{2}{5} ℓ = \frac{2}{5} ℓ$ $\frac{1}{2} \times \frac{2}{5} ℓ = \frac{1}{5} ℓ$

$1\frac{1}{2} \times \frac{2}{5} = \frac{3}{5}$

Miss Terry needs ⬜ ℓ of acid for the experiment.

6. Mr. Holmes took $\frac{1}{2}$ h to travel from Town A to Town B. He took $2\frac{1}{3}$ times this amount of time to travel from Town B to Town C. How long did he take to travel from Town B to Town C?

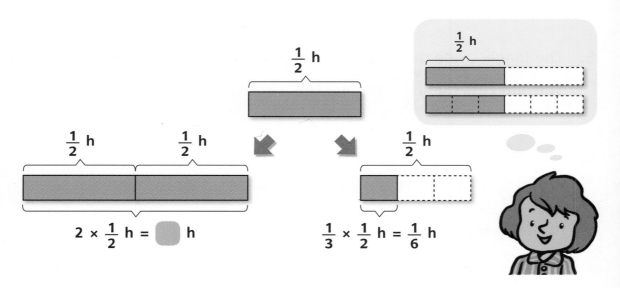

$2 \times \frac{1}{2} h = \boxed{} h$ $\frac{1}{3} \times \frac{1}{2} h = \frac{1}{6} h$

7. Mary has a ribbon $\frac{2}{3}$ m long. Rebecca has a ribbon that is $3\frac{1}{4}$ times as long as Mary's ribbon. What is the length of Rebecca's ribbon?

8. Gilbert made $\frac{a}{4}$ ℓ of lemonade with lemon syrup and water. How much lemon syrup did he use if $\frac{1}{3}$ of the lemonade consists of water?

$$\frac{a}{4} \times \frac{1}{3} = \frac{\boxed{}}{12}$$

He used ⬜ ℓ of lemon syrup.

9. Angel invented a method to multiply fractions.

$$\frac{1}{4} \times \frac{2}{3}$$

Double $\frac{1}{4}$ to get $\frac{1}{2}$.
Halve $\frac{2}{3}$ to get $\frac{1}{3}$.

$\frac{1}{2} \times \frac{1}{3}$

Double $\frac{1}{2}$ to get 1.
Halve $\frac{1}{3}$ to get $\frac{1}{6}$.

$1 \times \frac{1}{6}$

Explain why Angel's method works.

Exercise 4, pages 52 - 53

Jacob, Miguel, Emily and Mishon shared $\frac{2}{3}$ of a pizza. What fraction of the pizza did each of them get?

Method 1:

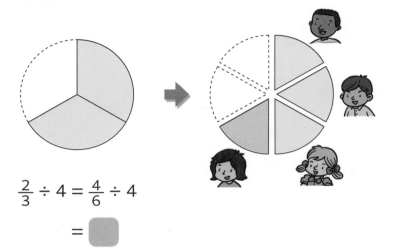

$\frac{2}{3} \div 4 = \frac{4}{6} \div 4$

$= \boxed{}$

Each of them got $\boxed{}$ of the pizza.

Method 2:

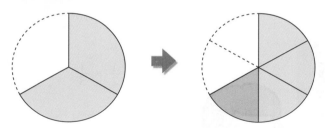

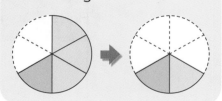

A quarter of $\frac{2}{3}$ is the same as half of $\frac{1}{3}$.

$\frac{2}{3} \div 4 = \frac{1}{4} \times \frac{2}{3}$

$= \frac{1}{2} \times \frac{1}{3}$

$= \boxed{}$

We can also write it like this:

$\frac{1}{\underset{2}{\cancel{4}}} \times \frac{\overset{1}{\cancel{2}}}{3}$

Each of them got $\boxed{}$ of the pizza.

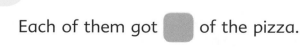

10. Luke has a $\frac{1}{2}$-yd rope. He cuts the rope into 5 equal pieces. What is the length of each piece?

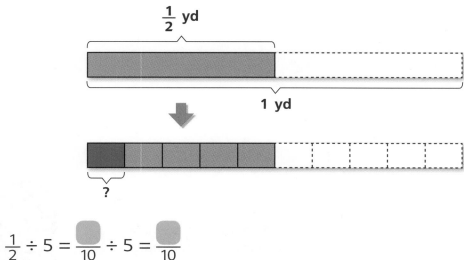

$$\frac{1}{2} \div 5 = \frac{\boxed{}}{10} \div 5 = \frac{\boxed{}}{10}$$

The length of each piece is $\boxed{}$ yd.

11. $\frac{3}{4}$ of the students in a class are girls. These girls are separated into 9 groups. What fraction of the students is each group of girls?

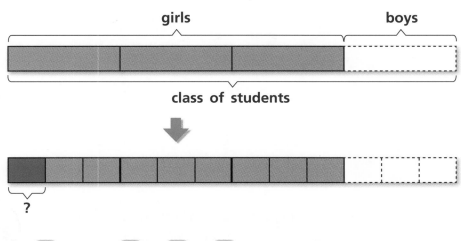

$$\frac{3}{4} \div 9 = \frac{\boxed{}}{9} \times \frac{3}{4} = \frac{\boxed{}}{3} \times \frac{\boxed{}}{4} = \frac{\boxed{}}{12}$$

In each group, $\boxed{}$ of the students are girls.

12. Chelsea has 5 apple tarts. She cuts each tart into $\frac{1}{2}$. Find the number of half-tarts Chelsea has.

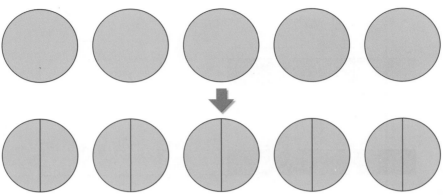

$5 \div \frac{1}{2} = 10$

When you cut a whole into halves, you get 2 halves. So, in 5 wholes there are 5 × 2 halves.

Chelsea has  half-tarts.

13. 3 cakes are shared equally among some children. Each child gets $\frac{3}{4}$ of a cake. How many children got $\frac{3}{4}$ of a cake?

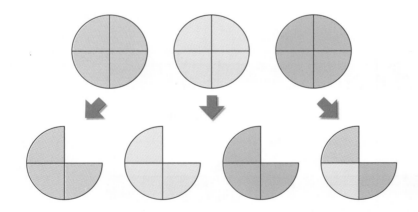

$3 \div \frac{3}{4} = 4$

When you cut a whole into three-quarters, you get $1\frac{1}{3}$ three-quarters. So, in 3 wholes there are $3 \times 1\frac{1}{3}$ three-quarters.

 children shared the cakes.

14. Jerome has a $\frac{3}{4}$-m ribbon. He cuts the ribbon into equal pieces $\frac{1}{8}$ m long. How many $\frac{1}{8}$-m-long pieces of ribbon does Jerome have?

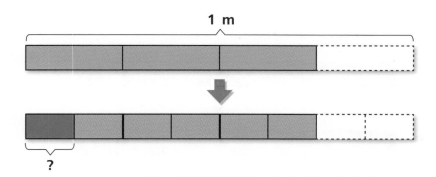

1 m

?

When you cut a whole into eighths, you get 8 eighths. So, in $\frac{3}{4}$ there are $\frac{3}{4}$ × 8 eighths.

$$\frac{3}{4} \div \frac{1}{8} = \boxed{}$$

Jerome has $\boxed{}$ $\frac{1}{8}$-m-long pieces of ribbon.

15. Hillary has $\frac{9}{10}$ ℓ of cooking oil. She pours them into $\frac{1}{20}$-ℓ bottles. Find the number of $\frac{1}{20}$-ℓ bottles of cooking oil Hillary has.

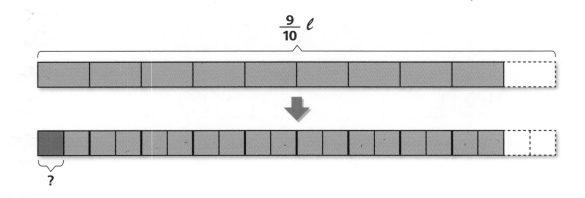

$\frac{9}{10}$ ℓ

?

$$\frac{9}{10} \div \frac{1}{20} = \boxed{}$$

Hillary has $\boxed{}$ $\frac{1}{20}$-ℓ bottles of cooking oil.

16. Blake has a $3\frac{1}{2}$-m string. He cuts the string into $\frac{1}{2}$-m pieces. How many pieces of $\frac{1}{2}$-m string does he have?

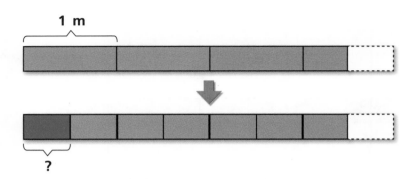

$$3\frac{1}{2} \text{ m} \div \frac{1}{2} \text{ m} = \boxed{}$$

He has ⬜ pieces of $\frac{1}{2}$-m string.

17. Keira bought $2\frac{1}{2}$ kg of flour. She packs the flour into $\frac{5}{12}$-kg bags. How many $\frac{5}{12}$-kg bags of flour does she have?

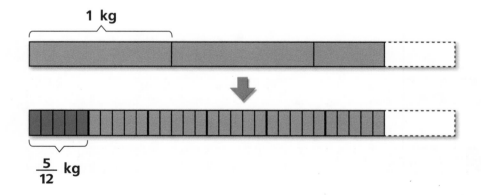

$$2\frac{1}{2} \text{ kg} \div \frac{5}{12} \text{ kg} = \boxed{}$$

She has ⬜ $\frac{5}{12}$-kg bags of flour.

18. Jake buys $4\frac{2}{5}$ ℓ of milk. He pours all the milk into $\frac{3}{5}$-ℓ containers.

How many containers are completely filled? What fraction of the last container is filled?

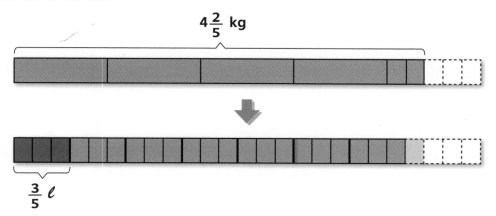

$4\frac{2}{5}$ kg

$\frac{3}{5}$ ℓ

19. How many times is $\frac{5}{6}$ as large as $\frac{1}{3}$?

$\frac{5}{6} \div \frac{1}{3} = $

20. Todd reasons that

$$\frac{2}{3} \div 4 = \frac{1}{4} \times \frac{2}{3}$$
$$= \frac{1}{2} \times \frac{1}{3}$$
$$= \frac{1}{6}.$$

With the help of the diagrams, explain Todd's reasoning.

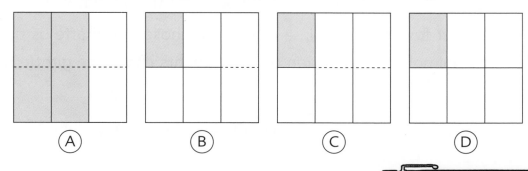

A   B   C   D

69

Exercise 6, pages 57 - 58

1. Find the value of each of the following.
   (a) $\frac{1}{4} \times 48$

   (b) $\frac{3}{5} \times 120$

   (c) $\frac{1}{3} \times \frac{3}{5}$

   (d) $\frac{2}{3} \times \frac{3}{4}$

   (e) $\frac{2}{3} \times 1\frac{3}{4}$

   (f) $2\frac{1}{2} \times \frac{3}{8}$

   (g) $\frac{5}{8} \div 5$

   (h) $\frac{3}{4} \div 4$

   (i) $5 \div \frac{1}{3}$

   (j) $\frac{2}{7} \div \frac{5}{7}$

   (k) $\frac{2}{3} \div \frac{3}{4}$

   (l) $\frac{3}{4} \div \frac{2}{3}$

2. Alan has 27 apples. He gives $\frac{1}{3}$ of his apples to Marilyn. How many apples does Alan give to Marilyn?

3. Javier has $\frac{3}{4}$ carton of drinks. He shared the drinks equally with Feliciano. There are 24 cans of drinks in each carton. How many cans of drinks does Feliciano have?

4. In a science experiment, $\frac{3}{4} \ell$ of a liquid is poured equally into 4 beakers. Find the volume of the liquid in each beaker.

5. Mrs. Leighton has 5 dozen muffins. She packs the muffins into bags of $\frac{1}{4}$ dozen. How many bags of muffins does Mrs. Leighton have?

6. Atsu bought a rope that is $9\frac{1}{3}$ yd long. Jerome bought a rope that is $\frac{1}{4}$ the length of Atsu's rope. What is the total length of the ropes that Atsu and Jerome bought?

7. A class of 40 students went to the zoo. $\frac{5}{8}$ of the students chose the lion as their favorite animal. $\frac{1}{2}$ of the rest chose the giraffe as their favorite animal. What fraction of the students chose the giraffe as their favorite animal?

8. Two cakes weigh a total of $5\frac{3}{8}$ kg. One of the cakes weighs $1\frac{5}{8}$ kg less than the other. Find the weight of the heavier cake.

REVIEW 2

1. State the smallest and greatest numbers.

    (a) 0.7, 0.63, $\frac{2}{3}$, $\frac{3}{4}$

    (b) 1.5, 1.41, $1\frac{4}{5}$, $1\frac{4}{7}$

    (c) -4.3, -4.29, $-4\frac{1}{2}$, $-4\frac{1}{3}$

    (d) -0.2, -0.5, $-\frac{2}{5}$, $-\frac{2}{7}$

    (e) 0, $-\frac{2}{5}$, $1\frac{5}{7}$, $-2\frac{1}{4}$

2. The given numbers are placed on a number line.

    (a) 1.8, $\frac{7}{8}$, $-\frac{9}{10}$, $-1\frac{1}{2}$, $1\frac{2}{5}$

    (i) Which two numbers are closest to each other?
    (ii) Which two numbers are furthest from each other?

    (b) -1.75, 2.5, $-1\frac{7}{10}$, $2\frac{5}{6}$

    Which two numbers are closest to 2?

    (c) 0, -2.3, -3.4, $-2\frac{3}{5}$, $-3\frac{1}{4}$

    Which two numbers are closest to each other?

3. Draw a number line.

    (a) Show the positions of 0, $1\frac{3}{4}$ and $-1\frac{1}{3}$.

    (b) Find the difference between $1\frac{3}{4}$ and $-1\frac{1}{3}$.

4. Find the perimeter of each figure.

    (a)

    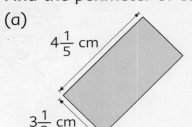

    $4\frac{1}{5}$ cm

    $3\frac{1}{3}$ cm

    (b)

    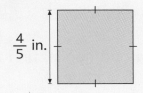

    $\frac{4}{5}$ in.

    (c)

    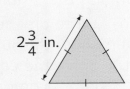

    $2\frac{3}{4}$ in.

5. (a) Find the least common multiple of 2, 3 and 4.

   (b) Find the value of $\frac{1}{2} + \frac{1}{3} + \frac{1}{4}$.

6. (a) Find the value of $\frac{1}{3} - \frac{1}{6}$. Simplify $2\frac{b}{3} - \frac{b}{6}$.

   (b) Find the value of $\frac{2}{7} + \frac{3}{7}$. Simplify $\frac{a}{7} + 2\frac{a}{7}$.

   (c) Find the value of $\frac{1}{3} + \frac{1}{4}$. Simplify $\frac{c}{3} + \frac{c}{4}$.

   (d) Find the value of $\frac{5}{6} - \frac{3}{4}$. Simplify $\frac{d}{6} - \frac{d}{4}$.

7. Solve each equation.

   (a) $3x = 8$

   (b) $\frac{1}{8}x = 3$

   (c) $x + 3 = 8$

   (d) $8 - x = 3$

> Write an equation in terms of x that has the same solution as each equation.

8. The volume of a pyramid is given by the expression $\frac{1}{3}abh$. Find the volume of the pyramid when $a = 3$ inches, $b = \frac{45}{8}$ inches and $h = \frac{4}{9}$ inches.

9. In the expression, $d = \frac{m}{v}$, find the value of d when $m = 5$ and $v = \frac{1}{3}$.

> $\frac{m}{v}$ is the same as $m \div v$.

10. The sum of 5 **consecutive even numbers** is 230. Let x be the smallest number among the 5 numbers.

> 2, 4, 6 are consecutive even numbers.

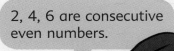

   (a) Write an equation, in terms of x, to show the sum.

   (b) Solve the equation and hence, find the largest among the 5 numbers.

11. A cake requires $1\frac{2}{3}$ kg of flour. Mrs. Neeson is baking 3 similar cakes. Find the amount of flour required.

72

Review 2, pages 59 - 62

4 PERCENTAGE

Think of different ways to find 80% of 120.

10% of 120 is 12.

80% of 120 is 8 × 12 = ▢ .

10% of 120 is 12.
20% of 120 is 24.

80% of 120 is 120 — 24 = ▢ .

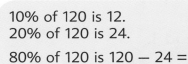

10% of 120 is 12.
20% of 120 is 24.
40% of 120 is 48.

80% of 120 is ▢ .

Think of different ways to find 25% of 210.

Think of different ways to find 95% of 98.

73

1 Percentage of a Quantity

There are 80 oranges in a box. 5% of the oranges are rotten. How many rotten oranges are there in the box?

80 oranges

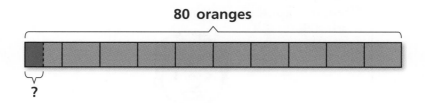

?

10% of 80 is 8.

5% of 80 is 4.

Method 1:

100% ⟶ 80
10% ⟶ 8
5% ⟶ 4

There are 4 rotten oranges in the box.

Method 2:

5% of 80 = $\frac{5}{100} \times 80$

= 4

There are 4 rotten oranges in the box.

How many oranges in the box are not rotten?

1. A school used 67% of a $9800 donation to buy library books. Find the amount used to buy library books.

Method 1:

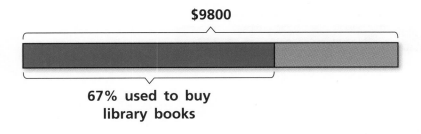

$9800

67% used to buy library books

100% ⟶ ☐

1% ⟶ ☐

67% ⟶ ☐

$☐ was used to buy library books.

Method 2:

$67\% \text{ of } 9800 = \dfrac{\boxed{}}{100} \times \boxed{}$

$= \boxed{}$

$☐ was used to buy library books.

2. There are 600 members in a club. 18% of the members are children. How many members are adults?

Method 1:

0%   18%   100%

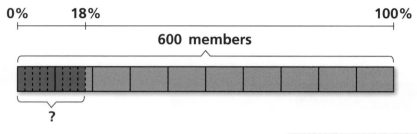

600 members

?

100% ⟶ 600

10% ⟶

1% ⟶ ☐

18% ⟶ ☐

1% ⟶ ☐
18% ⟶ 18 × ☐ = ☐

☐ members are children.

Alternatively,
$\frac{18}{100} \times 600 = $ ☐.

600 − ☐ = ☐

☐ members are adults.

Method 2:

100%

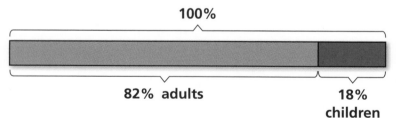

82% adults   **18% children**

100% ⟶ 600

10% ⟶ ☐

1% ⟶ ☐

☐ % ⟶ ☐ × ☐ = ☐

☐ members are adults.

18% and 82% add up to 100%.

Alternatively,
$\frac{82}{100} \times 600 = $ ☐.

76

Exercise 1, pages 63 - 64
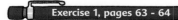

3. At a concert, 15% of the tickets were priced at \$120, 40% were priced at \$80 and the rest were priced at \$50. There were 4000 seats in the concert hall. How many tickets were priced at \$50?

Method 1:

100% ⟶ 4000

10% ⟶ ▢

5% ⟶ ▢

15% ⟶ ▢

40% ⟶ ▢

$\frac{15}{100} \times 4000 =$ ▢

$\frac{40}{100} \times 4000 =$ ▢

4000 − ▢ − ▢ = ▢

There were ▢ tickets priced at \$50.

Method 2:

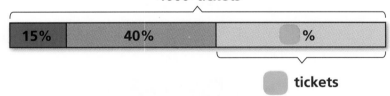

4000 tickets

| 15% | 40% | ▢ % |

▢ **tickets**

100% − 15% − 40% = ▢ %

100% ⟶ 4000

10% ⟶ ▢

5% ⟶ ▢

▢ % ⟶ ▢

Alternatively,

$\frac{▢}{100} \times 4000 =$ ▢.

There were ▢ tickets priced at \$50.

77

Exercise 2, pages 65 - 66

2 Percentage Change

The graph shows the scores at some Lakers' games.

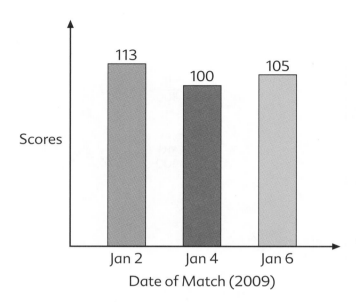

Scores (vertical axis)

- Jan 2: 113
- Jan 4: 100
- Jan 6: 105

Date of Match (2009)

(a) At the match on January 4, the Lakers scored 100 points against their opponents, a decrease from the match on January 2. Find the **percent decrease** in the scores from January 2 to January 4.

Jan 2 ⟶ 113
Jan 4 ⟶ 100
Change = 113 − 100
        = 13

113 points

Jan 2

Jan 4

100 points

Percent decrease = $\frac{13}{113} \times 100\%$

= 11.5%

There is an 11.5% decrease in the scores from January 2 to January 4.

(b) What is the **percent increase** in the Lakers' scores between the January 4 and January 6 matches?

Jan 4 ⟶ 100
Jan 6 ⟶ 105
Change = 105 − 100
= 5

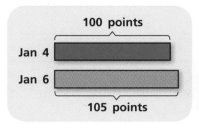

Percent increase = $\frac{5}{100}$ × 100%
= 5%

There is a 5% increase in the scores between the January 4 and January 6 matches.

(c) The Lakers' coach wants the team to improve their January 6 score by at least 10% in the next game. What is the minimum score that the team must get to achieve the coach's target?

Jan 6 ⟶ 105
Next game ⟶ ?
10% of 105 = 10.5

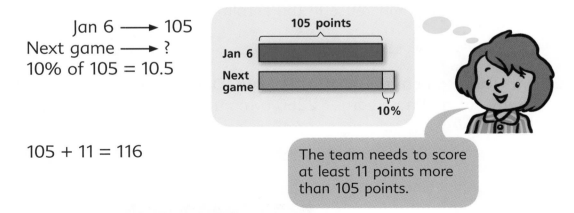

105 + 11 = 116

The team needs to score at least 11 points more than 105 points.

The team must score at least 116 points in the next match.

1. The table shows the enrolment of Greenfield School.

Year	Number of students
2007	800
2008	880

Find the percent increase in the enrolment between 2007 and 2008.

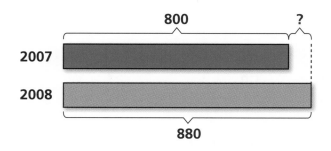

Change = ⬜

Percent increase = $\dfrac{⬜}{⬜}$ × 100%

= ⬜%

There is a ⬜% increase in the enrolment.

2. Mr. Thomson earned $2400 a month. During a recession, he accepted a pay cut and now earns $2260 a month. Find the percent decrease in his salary.

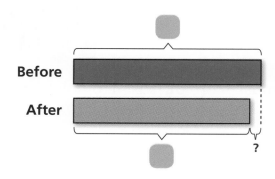

3.

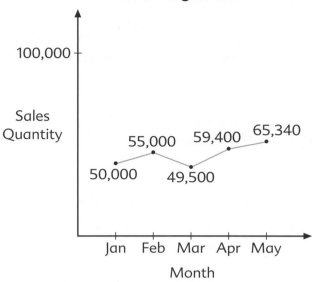

Shara Magazine Sales

(a) Complete the table.

	Percent increase or decrease
January to February	⬜ % increase/decrease
February to March	⬜ % increase/decrease
March to April	⬜ % increase/decrease
April to May	⬜ % increase/decrease

(b) Find the percent increase in the sales of Shara Magazine between January and May.

(c) It is projected that there is going to be a 15% increase in the sales of Shara Magazine in the month of June. How many copies of the magazine should be printed?

15% of ⬜ = $\frac{15}{100}$ × ⬜ = ⬜

⬜ + ⬜ = ⬜

The projected sales is ⬜ copies.

So, ⬜ copies of Shara Magazine should be printed.

Exercise 3, pages 67 - 68

1. There are 90 visitors at an art exhibition. 20% of the visitors are children. How many children visit the art exhibition?

2. A store sells 1800 cell phones in March. 3% of the cell phones are faulty. How many cell phones are faulty?

3. 160 children are in a summer camp. 45% of the children are boys. How many girls are there in the summer camp?

4. 700 immigrants took an English test. 88% of them passed the test. How many of them failed the test?

5. William collects 6000 stamps. 40% of the stamps are from England and 25% are from Canada. The other stamps are from countries in Asia. How many stamps from Asia does William have?

6. A store sells $5000 worth of running shoes on Monday. On Tuesday, it sells $6250 worth of running shoes. What is the percent increase in sales between Monday and Tuesday?

7. Mrs. Simpson ran 2000 m last week. This week, she runs 17% less than last week. What is the distance she runs this week?

8. A charity organization raised $20,000 in 2006. In 2007, there was a 35% increase in the funds it raised. A 17% decrease in the funds raised was reported in 2008. How much did the organization raise in 2008?

3 Simple Interest, Sales Tax and Discount I

1.

Alejandro bought the television set and paid a **sales tax** of 8%. How much did he pay for the television set?

8% of $ ⬜ = $ ⬜

The sales tax for the television set is $ ⬜ .

$900 + $ ⬜ = $ ⬜

Alejandro paid $ ⬜ for the television set.

2.

How much does Roberto have to pay for the pair of shorts?

20% of $45 = $ ⬜

The **discount** is $ ⬜ .

$ ⬜ − $ ⬜ = $ ⬜

Roberto has to pay $ ⬜ for the pair of shorts.

3.

Steak Delight
Restaurant
―――――――――

1 Steak	$22.00
1 Lime Juice	$2.00
Total	$24.00

Mr. Kellman gave the waiter 15% of the bill as a tip. How much money did Mr. Kellman spend in the restaurant altogether?

15% of $24 = $ ☐

Mr. Kellman gave the waiter $ ☐ as a tip.

$ ☐ + $ ☐ = $ ☐

Mr. Kellman spent $ ☐ altogether.

4. Kelly puts $3000 in an investment account for 5 years. She does not have further savings to or withdrawals from the account. Each year, she gets an **interest** of 12% per year of the amount she has in the account.

(a) What is the amount she has in the investment account after 1 year?

(b) If she saves the interest in the same account, what is the amount she has in the account after 5 years?

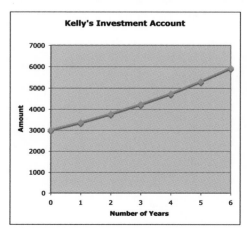

Kelly's Investment Account

Create a spreadsheet on a computer program to compute the amount Kelly has in the account after x years when x is a whole number.

Exercises 4 and 5, pages 69 - 72

1. Gabriel sells $20,000 worth of furniture in March. His **commission** is 15% of his sales in the month. How much money does Gabriel take home in commissions in March?

2. Logan earns $32,000. He pays a 7% **income tax**. How much does he pay for income tax?

3.

   How much does Abby pay for the jacket?

4. Jensen earns 2% interest per year on his fixed savings of $2500. What is the amount in his account after 1 year?

5.

   UP TOWN
   RESTAURANT

Fish N Chips	$ 10.95
Sirloin Steak	$ 25.00
Salad	$ 6.00
Roasted Chicken	$ 31.55
Carrot Juice	$ 3.50
Hot Chocolate	$ 2.50
Subtotal	: $79.50
Tax 8.5 %	:

   Calculate the total amount paid.

4 Simple Interest, Sales Tax and Discount II

Mindy paid $88 for a coffee maker, inclusive of sales tax. The sales tax is 10%. What was the price of the coffee maker excluding the sales tax?

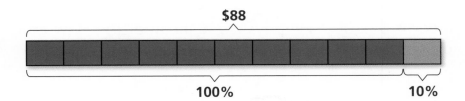

$88

100%   10%

11 units ⟶ $88
1 unit ⟶ $8
10 units ⟶ $80

The coffee maker cost $80 excluding the sales tax.

1. Francisco gets a monthly allowance from his mother. This month, his mother increases his allowance and gives him $75, which is 25% more than his previous allowance. How much allowance did he receive previously?

Method 1:

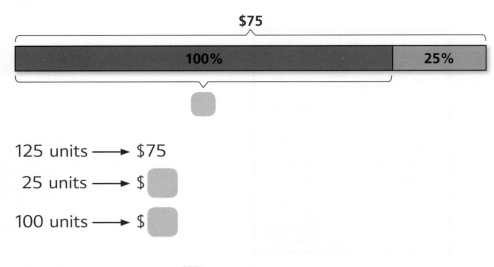

$75

100%   25%

125 units ⟶ $75

25 units ⟶ $ ☐

100 units ⟶ $ ☐

Francisco received $ ☐ allowance previously.

Method 2:

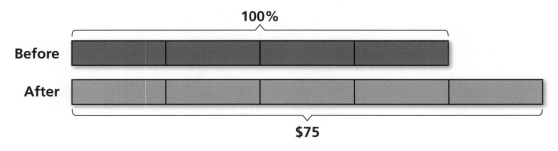

Before

After

100%

$75

5 units ⟶ $75

1 unit ⟶ $ ▢

4 units ⟶ $ ▢

100 : 25 = 4 : 1
4 units + 1 unit = 5 units

Francisco received $ ▢ allowance previously.

2. A store orders some boxes of a new brand of cereal from their supplier. The supplier gives the store an additional 3% of the number of boxes ordered as free samples for customers. The store receives 1648 boxes in all. How many boxes of cereal did the store order?

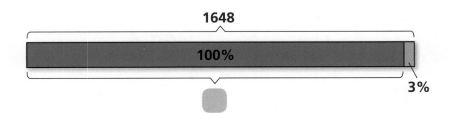

1648

100%

3%

103% ⟶ 1648

1% ⟶ ▢

100% ⟶ ▢

The store ordered ▢ boxes of cereal.

3. Mr. Robertson buys a camera with an extended warranty for $456. The extended warranty costs 14% of the price of the camera. How much does Mr. Robertson pay for only the camera?

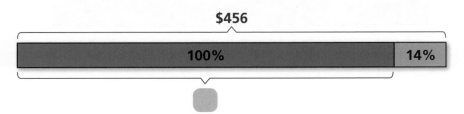

$456

| 100% | 14% |

4. In the year 2006, there were 37,852 new reported cases of HIV infection. This was a 5% decrease from the year 2000. Find the number of new reported cases in the year 2000.

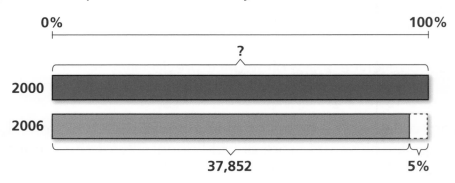

0%   100%

?
2000

2006
37,852   5%

5. This is an excerpt of a newspaper article.

Customers prefer house brands

The results of a survey of 100 households pointed to shoppers having a preference for house brand products in supermarkets. It showed that of 280 households with a combined income of at least $6000 per month, 71 reported buying house brand products from June to December. This is compared to 60 during the preceding 6 months – an increase of x%.

Supermarket	Product	House brand	Commercial brand
Lo-Cost	Cooking oil	$5.46 (2 qt)	$8.10 (2 qt)
Kelly's	Bread	$1.60 (1 lb)	$1.85 (1 lb)

(a) Calculate the value of x.
(b) Find the values of y and z.
  (i) The commercial brand cooking oil costs y% more than the house brand one.
  (ii) The commercial brand bread costs z% more than the house brand one.

Exercise 6, pages 73 - 74

1. The selling price of a dining table is $520. This is 30% more than its cost price. What is the cost price of the dining table?

2. Victoria saves $120 this month. This is 5% more than the amount she saved last month. How much money did Victoria save last month?

3. A charity organizer orders some muffins. Celso bakes 2500 muffins, 2% more than what is ordered. How many muffins are ordered for the charity event?

4. A company employs some people. It needs to employ 1116 people in all, 24% more people than what it is employing now. How many people does the company employ now?

5.

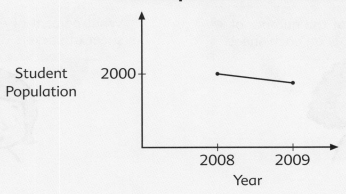

Student Population at Charlton High

The student population in Charlton High drops 12% between 2008 and 2009. What is the student population at Charlton High in 2009?

5 RATIO AND PROPORTION

What fraction of each sheet of stickers are 🖤?

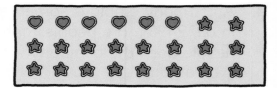

What is the **ratio** of the number of 🖤 to the number of ⭐ on each sheet?

What percent of each sheet of stickers are 🖤?

Is the number of stickers on one sheet in **proportion** to that of another?

What does it mean when we say that the number of 🖤 is in proportion to the number of ⭐?

① Comparing Quantities I

Bella has 3 pencils. Andy has 1 pencil.

Bella has 3 times as many pencils as Andy.
The ratio of the number of Bella's pencils to the number of Andy's pencils is 3 : 1.

We read the ratio 3 : 1 as **3 to 1**.

We can also say that:

Andy has $\frac{1}{3}$ the number of pencils that Bella has.

The ratio of the number of Andy's pencils to the number of Bella's pencils is 1 : 3.

1. The ratio of the number of red apples to the number of green apples is 4 : 1.

There are ⬜ times as many red apples as green apples.

The ratio of the number of green apples to the number of red apples is ⬜ : ⬜ .

There are ⬜ as many green apples as red apples.

91

2. There are 4 boys and 2 girls.

The ratio of the number of boys to the number of girls is 4 : 2.

The number of boys is twice the number of girls.
We can also say that the ratio of the number of boys to the number of girls is 2 : 1.

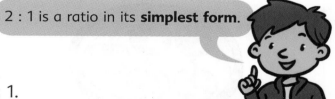

2 : 1 is a ratio in its **simplest form**.

So, 4 : 2 = 2 : 1.

The number of girls is ▢ the number of boys.

The ratio of the number of girls to the number of boys is ▢ : ▢ .

So, 2 : 4 = 1 : ▢ .

3. There are 9 chairs and 3 tables.

The ratio of the number of chairs to the number of tables is 9 : 3.

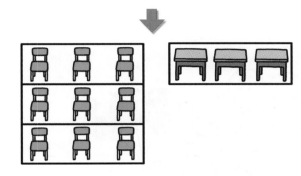

There are three times as many chairs as tables.
The ratio of the number of chairs to the number of tables is

also [ ] : 1.

So, 9 : 3 = [ ] : [ ].

The answer is a ratio expressed in the simplest form.

4. Alfred has some marbles.

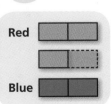

The ratio of the number of blue marbles to the number of red marbles is 2 : 3.

The number of blue marbles is [ ] that of red marbles.

The ratio of the number of red marbles to the number of blue marbles is 3 : 2.

The number of red marbles is [ ] times that of blue marbles.

Exercise 1, pages 75 - 76

1.

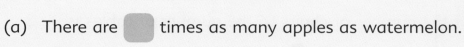
Write each ratio in its simplest form.

(a) There are ☐ times as many apples as watermelon.

(b) Find the ratio of the number of apples to the watermelon.

2.

(a) The number of green balloons is ☐ the number of yellow balloons.

(b) Find the ratio of the number of green balloons to the number of yellow balloons.

(c) Find the ratio of the number of yellow balloons to the total number of balloons.

3.

(a) There are ☐ times as many black markers as blue markers.

(b) Find the ratio of the number of black markers to the number of blue markers.

(c) There are ☐ as many blue markers as black markers.

(d) Find the ratio of the number of blue markers to the number of black markers.

4.

(a) The number of books is ▢ the number of files.

(b) Find the ratio of the number of books to the number of files. Express the answer in the simplest form.

(c) The number of files is ▢ times the number of books.

(d) Find the ratio of the number of files to the number of books in the simplest form.

5. Brian has 5 game CDs and 15 music CDs. Find the ratio, in the simplest form, of the number of game CDs to the number of music CDs.

6. There are 20 girls and 15 boys in a class. Find the ratio of the number of girls to the number of boys. Express the answer in the simplest form.

7. Gillian has 4 times as many stamps as Tania. What is the ratio of the number of stamps Gillian has to the number of stamps Tania has? Express the answer in the simplest form.

8. Wayne has $\frac{2}{3}$ as many pencils as pens. What is the ratio of the number of pens to the number of pencils? Express the answer in the simplest form.

9. Write each ratio in its simplest form.
   (a) 2 : 6
   (b) 16 : 4
   (c) 6 : 9
   (d) 25 : 15

2 Comparing Quantities II

There are 5 times as many nickels as quarters.
The ratio of the number of nickels to quarters is 5 : 1.

Five nickels is worth a quarter.

The value of the nickels is the same as the value of the quarter.
The ratio of the value of the nickels to the value of the quarter is 1 : 1.

1.   String A is 12 cm long. String B is 2 cm long.

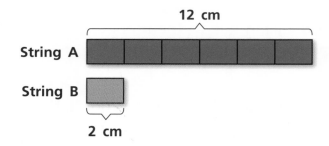

String A is 6 times as long as String B.

The ratio of the length of String A to the length of String B is : 1.

String B is ⬛ the length of String A.

The ratio of the length of String B to the length of String A is 1 : .

2. Kiera is 4 ft tall. Her younger brother, Ben, is 3 ft tall.

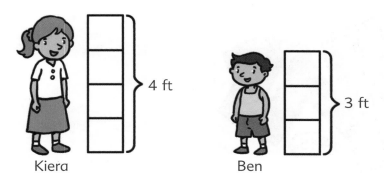

Kiera   Ben

Ben's height is ⬜ Kiera's height.

The ratio of Ben's height to Kiera's height is ⬜ : ⬜.

Kiera's height is ⬜ times Ben's height.

The ratio of Kiera's height to Ben's height is ⬜ : ⬜.

3. Bag X is 15 kg. Bag Y is 45 kg.

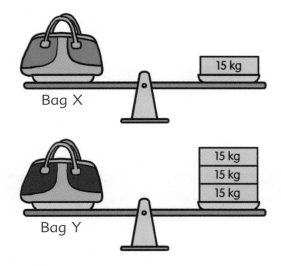

Bag X is 3 times as heavy as Bag X.

Bag Y is 3 times as heavy as Bag X.

The ratio of the weight of Bag X to the weight of Bag Y is ⬜ : ⬜.

Bag X is ⬜ the weight of Bag Y.

The ratio of the weight of Bag Y to the weight of Bag X is ⬜ : ⬜.

4. A pair of pants costs $27. A jacket costs $45.

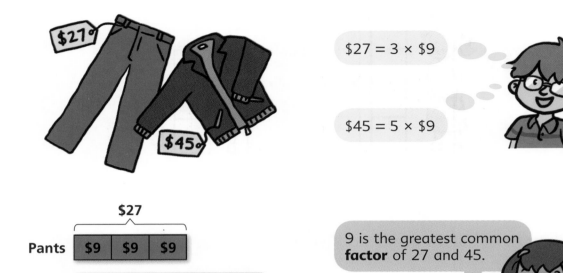

$27 = 3 × $9

$45 = 5 × $9

9 is the greatest common **factor** of 27 and 45.

The ratio of the cost of the pants to the cost of the jacket is ⬜ : ⬜.

The ratio of the cost of the jacket to the cost of the pants is ⬜ : ⬜.

5. Rod A is 20 cm long. Rod B is 1 m long.

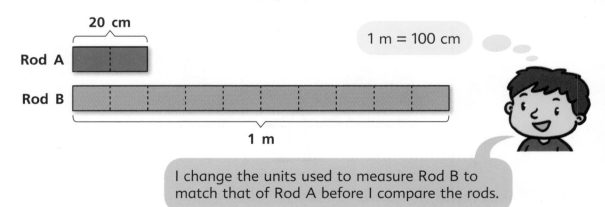

1 m = 100 cm

I change the units used to measure Rod B to match that of Rod A before I compare the rods.

Rod B is 5 times as long as Rod A.

The ratio of the length of Rod B to the length of Rod A is ⬜ : ⬜.

The ratio of the length of Rod A to the length of Rod B is ⬜ : ⬜.

6. Container E has 1 ℓ of water. Container F has 250 ml of water.

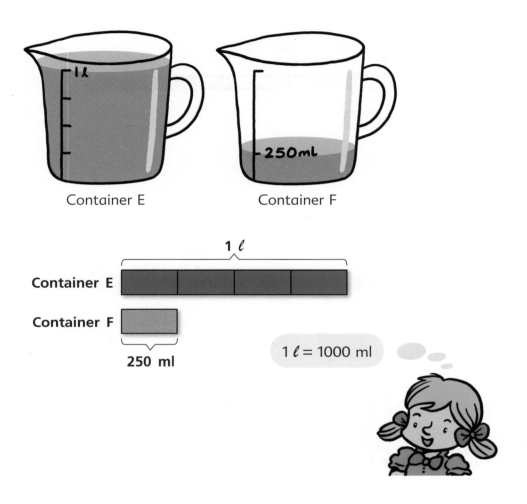

Container E   Container F

1 ℓ

Container E

Container F

250 ml

1 ℓ = 1000 ml

Container E has 4 times the amount of water as Container F.

The ratio of the amount of water in Container E to the amount of water in Container F is ⬜ : ⬜.

Container F has ⬜ the amount of water as Container E.

The ratio of the amount of water in Container F to the amount of water in Container E is ⬜ : ⬜.

Exercise 2, pages 77 - 78

1. An eraser is 1 in. long. A pencil is 8 in. long.

Find the ratio of the length of the pencil to the length of the eraser.

2. Figure A and B are made up of identical squares.

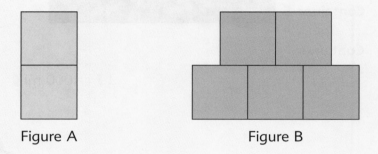

Figure A   Figure B

(a) The area of Figure A is ___ the area of Figure B.

(b) Find the ratio of the area of Figure A to the area of Figure B.

3. A barrel has 25 gal of water. A fish tank has 20 gal of water. Find the ratio of the amount of water in the barrel to the amount of water in the fish tank.

4. Helen saved $60 in six months. Fred saved $72 within the same period of time. Find the ratio of Helen's savings to Fred's savings.

5.

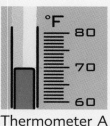

Thermometer A   Thermometer B

(a) The reading on Thermometer A is ▢ times that of the reading on Thermometer B.

(b) Find the ratio of the reading on Thermometer A to the reading on Thermometer B.

6.

(a) The tomatoes weigh ▢ as much as the potatoes.

(b) Find the ratio of the weight of tomatoes to the weight of potatoes.

7. Trent ran $1\frac{1}{2}$ times as far as his sister. What is the ratio of the distance Trent ran to the distance his sister ran?

8. A storybook costs $\frac{2}{7}$ as much as a storybook and a dictionary together. What is the ratio of the cost of the dictionary to the cost of the storybook?

9. Write each ratio in its simplest form.
   (a) 15 cm to 25 cm
   (b) 40 kg to 16 kg
   (c) $10 to $75
   (d) 25¢ to $1
   (e) 9 in. to 1 ft
   (f) 500 ml to 1.5 ℓ   1500

3 Comparing Three Quantities

On a farm, there are 2 horses, 4 dogs and 10 sheep.

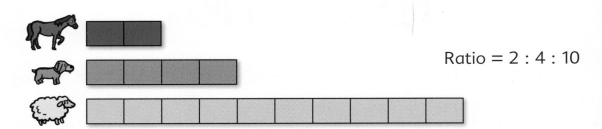

Ratio = 2 : 4 : 10

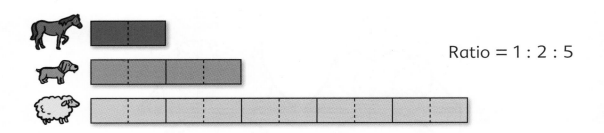

Ratio = 1 : 2 : 5

2 : 4 : 10 = 1 : 2 : 5

The ratio of the number of horses to the number of dogs to the number of sheep on the farm is 1 : 2 : 5.

1. Simplify 6 : 9 : 12.

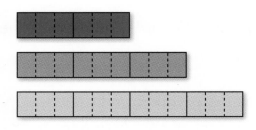

6 : 9 : 12 = ☐ : ☐ : ☐

2. Simplify 8 : 4 : 16.

102

Exercise 3, pages 79 - 80

3. There are twice as many adults as there are children in a room. The number of boys is $\frac{2}{3}$ that of girls.

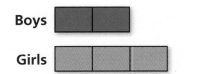

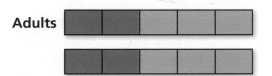

Find the ratio of the number of boys to the number of girls to the number of adults in the room.

Ratio = ⬜ : ⬜ : ⬜

b) Find $a : b : c$ if $a : b = 3 : 2$ and $b : c = 2 : 5$.

So, $a : b : c = 3 : 2 : 5$.

c) Find $x : y : z$ if $x : y = 2 : 3$ and $y : z = 2 : 3$.

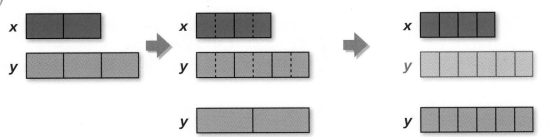

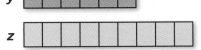

$x : y \quad = 4 : 6$
$\quad y : z = \quad 6 : 9$

So, $x : y : z = 4 : 6 : 9$.

4. Given that x : y = 4 : 5 and y : z = 10 : 7, find x : y : z.

x ▮▮▮▮

y ▮▮▮▮▮

$4 : 5 =$ ⬜ $: 10$

$x : y \quad =$ ⬜ $: 10$
$\quad y : z =$ $\quad 10 : 7$

So, $x : y : z =$ ⬜ $:$ ⬜ $:$ ⬜.

5. Given that $p : q = 4 : 5$ and $q : r = 3 : 1$, find $p : q : r$.

p ▮▮▮▮

q ▮▮▮▮▮▮

q ▮▮▮▮▮▮

r ▯

$4 : 5 =$ ⬜ $: 15$

$p : q \quad =$ ⬜ $: 15$

$\quad q : r =$ $\quad 15 :$ ⬜

So, the ratio of $p : q : r =$ ⬜ $:$ ⬜ $:$ ⬜.

6. Given that $a : b = 3 : 4$ and $b : c$ is $2 : 3$, find $a : b : c$.

$$\frac{9\ 3}{3\ 4} \quad \frac{B}{C}\ \frac{2}{3} \times \frac{2}{2} \quad \frac{4}{6} = 3 ; 4 : 6$$

7. Given that $s : t : u = 1 : 4 : 2$, find
(a) $s : t$
(b) $s : u$
(c) $t : u$

Exercise 4, pages 81 - 82

1. Find the missing numbers.

   (a) $3 : 5 : 4 = 9 : \boxed{} : 12$

   (b) $2 : 5 : 1 = \boxed{} : 20 : \boxed{}$

   (c) $\boxed{} : 4 : 6 = 4 : 2 : \boxed{}$

2.

	Boys	Girls
Grade 5	$p = 9$	$q = 15$
Grade 6	$r = 12$	$s = 18$

   Write each ratio in its simplest form and say what it stands for.
   (a) $p : q$ (b) $p : r$
   (c) $p + r : q : s$ (d) $p + q : r : s$

3. Given that $a : b = 2 : 9$ and $b : c = 3 : 5$, find $a : b : c$.

4. Given that $x : y = 1 : 2$ and $y : z = 5 : 2$, find $x : y : z$.

5. Given that $m : n = 3 : 4$ and $n : p = 3 : 5$, find the value of p when $m = 9$.

6. The table shows the number of different fruits in a fruit basket.

Fruits	Number
Oranges	4
Cherries	12
Grapefruit	3
Apples	8

   Write each ratio in its simplest form.
   (a) Number of oranges to cherries to grapefruits.
   (b) Number of oranges to cherries to apples.
   (c) Number of cherries to the number of fruits in the basket.

4 Word Problems

At a camp, the ratio of the number of boys to the number of girls is 3 : 2. There are 18 boys. Find the number of girls.

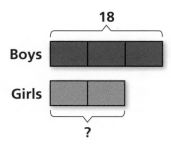

3 units ⟶ 18
1 unit ⟶ 6
2 units ⟶ 12

The number of girls is 12.

1. In a basketball game, the ratio of the opposing team's score to the home team's score is 3 : 5. The difference is 12 points. Find the opposing team's score.

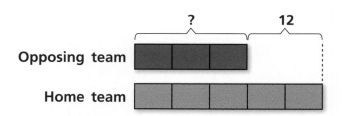

2 units ⟶ 12

1 unit ⟶ ☐

3 units ⟶ ☐

The opposing team's score is ☐.

2. 50 kg of flour was packed into 2 bags in the ratio of 2 : 5.
   Find the difference in weight between the 2 bags.

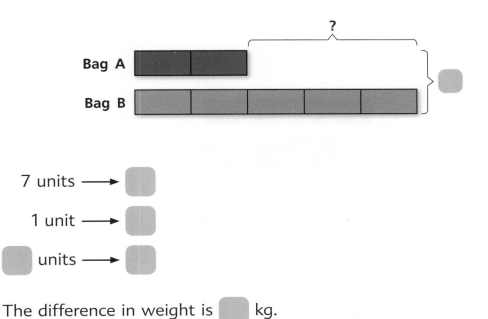

7 units $\longrightarrow$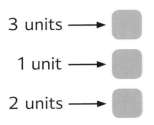

1 unit $\longrightarrow$

 units $\longrightarrow$

The difference in weight is kg.

3. A 51-m wire is cut in the ratio of 1 : 2.
   Find the length of the longer piece.

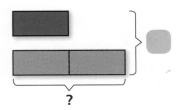

3 units $\longrightarrow$

1 unit $\longrightarrow$

2 units $\longrightarrow$

The length of the longer piece is m.

4. Marco has 84 coins that are either dimes or quarters.
   The ratio of the number of dimes to the number of quarters is 3 : 4.

   (a) Find the number of dimes.
   (b) Calculate the value of Marco's coins.

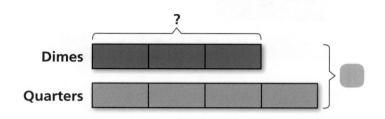

(a)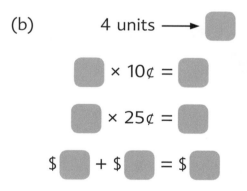

    □ units ⟶ □

    1 unit ⟶ □

    3 units ⟶ □

    Marco has □ dimes.

(b)   4 units ⟶ □

       □ × 10¢ = □

       □ × 25¢ = □

    $□ + $□ = $□

    The value of Marco's coins is $□.

5. There are 450 students in a school. The ratio of the number of teachers to the number of students is 1 : 15. The ratio of the number of male teachers to the number of female teachers is 1 : 4. Find the number of female teachers.

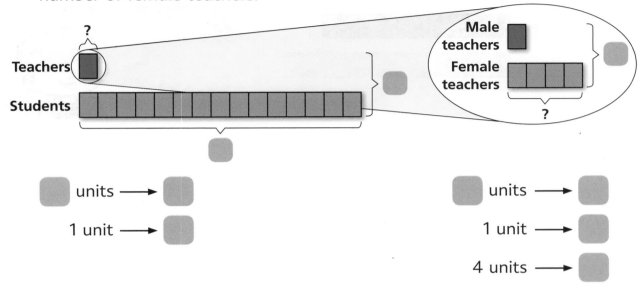

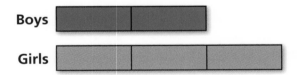

The number of female teachers is ⬜.

The ratio of the number of boys to the number of girls in a group is 2 : 3.

Boys

Girls

(a) After 6 boys joined the group, the ratio became 5 : 6. Find the number of boys at first.

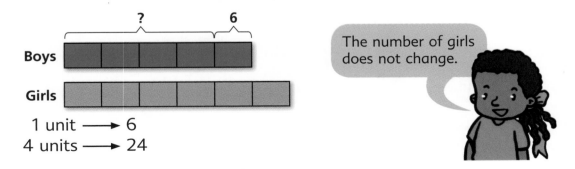

1 unit ⟶ 6
4 units ⟶ 24

There were 24 boys at first.

(b) Then, *p* girls left the group and the ratio became 2 : 1. Find the value of *p*.

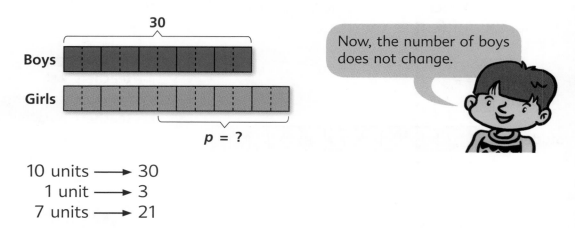

10 units ⟶ 30
1 unit ⟶ 3
7 units ⟶ 21

The value of *p* is 21.

6. John has US and foreign stamps in his album. The ratio of the number of US stamps to foreign stamps is 5 : 2. After Paul gives him 12 foreign stamps, the ratio becomes 2 : 1. Find the number of US stamps he has.

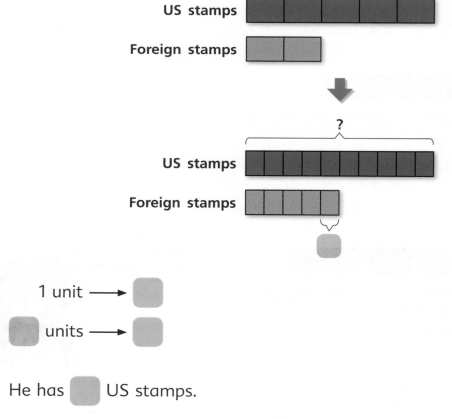

1 unit ⟶ ▢

▢ units ⟶ ▢

He has ▢ US stamps.

7. Wayne's savings to Stef's savings were in the ratio 5 : 6. After spending $28 each, the ratio became 1 : 4.

   (a) Find Wayne's savings before he spent $28.
   (b) Find Stef's savings after she spent $28.

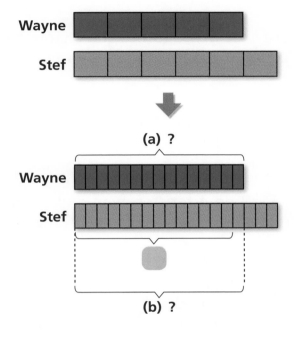

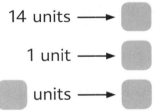

(a) Wayne's savings before he spent $28 was ⬜.

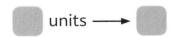

(b) Stef's savings after she spent $28 was ⬜.

111

Exercise 5, pages 83 - 85

1. In a quiz, the ratio of Carla's score to Mandy's score is 7 : 3. The difference between their score is 32 points. Find their total score.

2. The ratio of the distance Steve ran to the distance Hayley ran is 1 : 3. Steve ran 4.8 km. Find the distance Hayley ran.

3. Amanda cuts a 45-cm ribbon into two pieces in the ratio of 4 : 5. Find the length of the shorter piece.

4. Mrs. Green spent $128 on a toaster oven and an iron. The ratio of the cost of the toaster oven to the cost of the iron is 5 : 3. Find the cost of the toaster oven.

5. There are 840 students in a school. The ratio of the number of boys to the number of girls is 2 : 3. The ratio of the number of girls who wear glasses to the number of girls who do not wear glasses is 1 : 5. Find the number of girls who do not wear glasses.

6. In a train, the ratio of the number of males to the number of females is 5 : 6. At a train station, 8 males got off the train. The ratio of the number of males to the number of females is now 3 : 4. Find the number of people in the train now.

5 Proportion

Serving Size 8 fl oz

Calories 100

Protein 7 g

Total Fat 3.5 g

Cholesterol 0 mg

Total Carbohydrates 11 g

Dietary Fiber 2.4 g

Sodium 95 mg

Vitamin A 10 %

Vitamin C 0 %

Calcium 40 %

'fl oz' stands for fluid ounces. Fluid ounces are a unit of measurement of liquids.

Find the amount of dietary fiber in
(a) 40 fl oz of the soymilk.

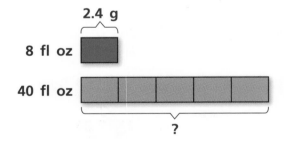

Amount of soymilk	Amount of dietary fiber
8 fl oz	2.4 g
16 fl oz	4.8 g
24 fl oz	g
32 fl oz	g
40 fl oz	g

8 fl oz ⟶ 2.4 g
40 fl oz ⟶ 5 × 2.4 g = 12 g

There are 12 g of dietary fiber in 40 fl oz of soymilk.

(b) 4 fl oz of the soymilk.

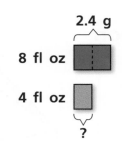

2.4 g

8 fl oz

4 fl oz

?

4 fl oz is $\frac{1}{2}$ of 8 fl oz.

$$\frac{4 \text{ fl oz}}{8 \text{ fl oz}} = \frac{1}{2}$$

The amount of dietary fiber in 4 fl oz (x grams) is $\frac{1}{2}$ the amount of dietary fiber in 8 fl oz (2.4 g).

$$\frac{x}{2.4} = \frac{1}{2}$$
$$x = 1.2$$

$$\frac{1}{2.4}x = \frac{1}{2}$$

$$x = 2.4 \times \frac{1}{2}$$

1.

Recipe

To serve 4
- 2 eggs
- 3 slices of bread

(a) How many eggs and slices of bread will serve 12 people?

To serve 4 people, we need 2 eggs and 3 slices of bread.

To serve 4,
2 eggs

Eggs

To serve 12, ⬜ eggs

To serve 4,
3 slices

Bread

To serve 12, ⬜ slices

To serve 12 (3 × 4), we need 3 × 2 = ⬜ eggs and

3 × 3 = ⬜ slices of bread.

(b) How many eggs and slices of bread will serve 2 people?

To serve 4 people, we need 2 eggs and 3 slices of bread.

To serve 2 ([ ] × 4), we need [ ] × 2 = [ ] egg and

[ ] × 3 = [ ] slices of bread.

2. To make a lemonade, Jane uses $\frac{1}{8}$ as much concentrate as water.

(a) How much concentrate does she need to make 720 ml of lemonade?

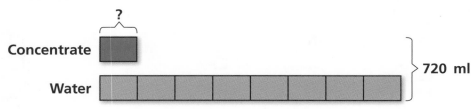

(b) How much concentrate does she need to make 1.8 ℓ of lemonade?

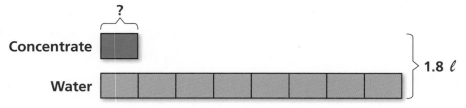

(c) How much concentrate does she need to make x ℓ of lemonade?

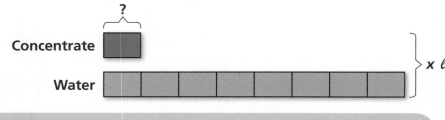

What do you notice about the ratio of the amount of concentrate to the amount of water when different amounts of lemonade are made?

3. Sandy makes a map of a pool area. She uses 1 cm to represent 250 cm.

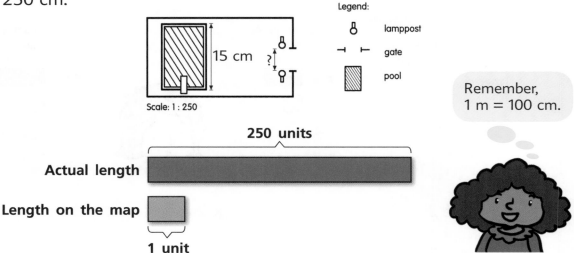

Legend:
- lamppost
- gate
- pool

Scale: 1 : 250

Remember, 1 m = 100 cm.

250 units

Actual length

Length on the map

1 unit

(a) On the map, the length of a pool is 15 cm. Find its actual length.

Let the actual length be a.

$$\frac{a}{15 \text{ cm}} = \frac{250}{1}$$

$$a = \boxed{} \times 15 \text{ cm}$$

$$= \boxed{}$$

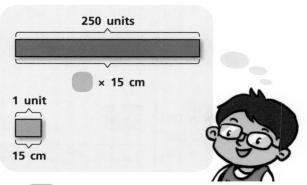

The actual length of the pool is $\boxed{}$ m.

(b) The distance between two lamp posts is 12.5 m. How far should these two lamp posts be drawn on the map?

Let the distance on the map be d.

$$\frac{d}{12.5 \text{ m}} = \frac{1}{250}$$

$$d = \boxed{} \times 12.5 \text{ m}$$

$$= \boxed{}$$

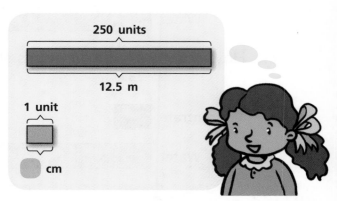

The two lamp posts should be $\boxed{}$ cm apart on the map.

4.

12 cm

20 cm

25 cm

A picture is **enlarged**.
Find the height of the building in the enlarged picture.

Method 1:

$$\frac{12}{\Box} \times \Box = \Box$$

The height of the building in the
enlarged picture is ⬚ cm.

Method 2:

The length of the building in the
original picture is $\frac{4}{5}$ the length of
the building in the enlarged picture.

$$\frac{20}{25} = \frac{4}{5} \qquad \frac{12}{\Box} = \frac{4}{5}$$

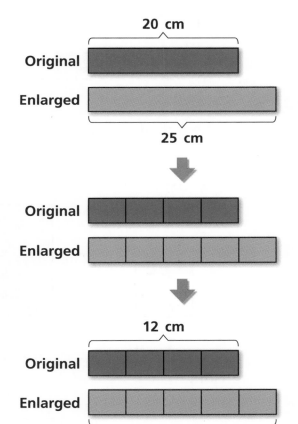

20 cm

Original

Enlarged

25 cm

Original

Enlarged

12 cm

Original

Enlarged

?

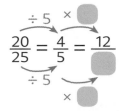

$$\underset{\div 5}{\overset{\times \Box}{\frac{20}{25}}} = \frac{4}{5} = \frac{12}{\Box}$$

The height of the building in the enlarged picture
is ⬚ cm.

117

Method 3:

In the enlarged picture, the length is increased by 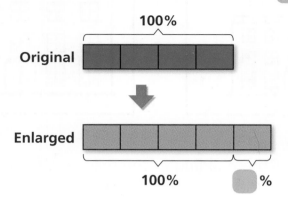%.

100%

Original

Enlarged

100% ▢%

increased by ▢%
20 cm ⟶ 25 cm

increased by ▢%
12 cm ⟶ ▢ cm

The height of the building in the enlarged place is ▢ cm.

5. The lengths and widths of three different sheets of stickers are given.

12 in.

6 in.

6 in.

6 in.

6 in.

12 in.

18 in.

Which sheets of stickers are in proportion to each other? Give your reason.

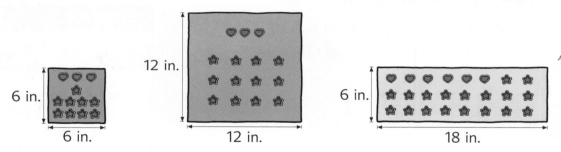

Ratio of length to width	6 : 6 = ▢ : ▢	▢ : ▢ = ▢ : ▢	▢ : ▢ = ▢ : ▢

118

Exercise 6, pages 86 - 88

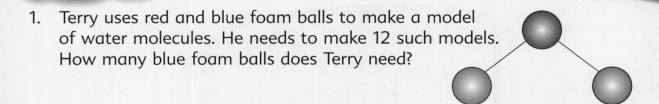

1. Terry uses red and blue foam balls to make a model of water molecules. He needs to make 12 such models. How many blue foam balls does Terry need?

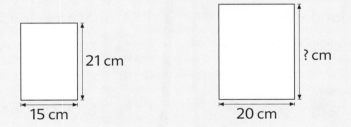

2. An artist makes a model of the Statue of Liberty that is $\frac{1}{50}$ of its original size.

   36 in.

   Find the actual height of the statue.

3. A 1 : 12 scale replica of a car measures 18 in. Find the actual length of the car.

4. A rectangle is enlarged using a copier.

   21 cm

   15 cm

   ? cm

   20 cm

   Find the length of the enlarged rectangle.

5. To make lemonade, Mrs. Anderson uses 1 pt of water and $\frac{1}{2}$ c of sugar for every 2 lemons.
   (a) If she uses 4 lemons, how much water will she need?
   (b) If she uses $3\frac{1}{2}$ qt of water, how many cups of sugar will she need?

6. This is a recipe for spaghetti and sweet corn fritters.

Ingredients (serves 6–8)
$1\frac{1}{2}$ cups spaghetti
A bunch of coriander leaves
$\frac{1}{2}$ cup sweet corn kernels
1 red chilli
2 tablespoons oyster sauce
3 eggs
Pepper to taste
5 tablespoons vegetable oil
Japanese mayonnaise

(a) Mrs. Yuki is making fritters for her family of 4. Suggest the amount of ingredients that she should use.

(b) Miss Tia is making some fritters for a party of 40. Suggest the amount of ingredients that she should use.

Ingredients
☐ cups spaghetti
A bunch of coriander leaves
☐ cup sweet corn kernels
☐ red chilli
☐ tablespoons oyster sauce
☐ eggs
Pepper to taste
☐ tablespoons vegetable oil
Japanese mayonnaise

Ingredients
☐ cups spaghetti
A bunch of coriander leaves
☐ cup sweet corn kernels
☐ red chilli
☐ tablespoons oyster sauce
☐ eggs
Pepper to taste
☐ tablespoons vegetable oil
Japanese mayonnaise

1. (a) Find 30% of $700.
   (b) Express 15 minutes as a percentage of 1 hour.

2. (a) Solve $\frac{n}{3} = 8$.
   (b) Solve $\frac{n}{5} = \frac{7}{20}$.

3.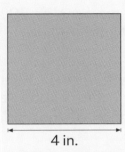

   2 in.

   4 in.

   (a) Find the ratio of the length of sides of the larger square to that of the smaller square.
   (b) Find the ratio of the area of larger square to that of the smaller square.

   What do you notice?

4.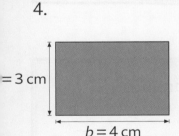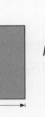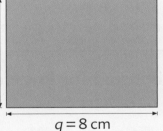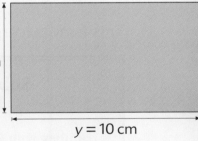

   $p = 6$ cm $x = 6$ cm

   $= 3$ cm

   $b = 4$ cm $q = 8$ cm $y = 10$ cm

   (a) Find the ratio of $a : p$ and $b : q$.
   (b) Find the ratio of $a : x$ and $b : y$.

5. A store is giving a 20% discount on selected items.
   (a) The original price of a bag is $86. Calculate the sale price of the bag.
   (b) The cashier uses his calculator to find the sale price. He keys in $0.8 \times \$86$. Explain why his method works.

6. The number of library books in a school increased by 20% after it bought new books in May. The number increased by another 20% after a bookstore donated 300 books in June. Find the number of books in the library before it bought new books in May.

7. In September, the ratio of the amount Ray spent and the amount he saved was 4 : 1. In October, he got a salary raise. He increased his spending by 25% but saved the same amount. Find the new ratio.

8. 25% of Ling's savings is the same amount as 20% of Neil's savings. Find the ratio of Ling's savings to Neil's savings.

9. As many as three instructors are hired for a martial arts class each week. A 4 : 1 student-to-instructor ratio is considered ideal. Find the maximum number of students at each of these classes.

10. Calculate the tax paid for breakfast. Express the answer to 2 decimal place.

Breakfast Club
The Mall
Friday APR 3 08:24
CHECK 451720

1 Breakfast	$4.20
Includes taxes 7%	
Total	$4.20
Change	$5.80
Dine In	

11. This is an excerpt taken from a newspaper article.

Subsidized housing for low-income families

By ANTHONY ARNOLD

Families with low income homes will soon be eligible for subsidized housing, under a statewide scheme spearheaded by local authorities.

The monthly rent is pegged to the combined income of the family members. To qualify, a family's monthly household income must fall below $2400. These families pay a monthly rent of 30% of their income.

(a) A family makes $25,200 a year. What would this family pay as a monthly rent?

(b) A family pays $540 a month in rent. What is the family's monthly income

Review 3, pages 89 - 93

30 km/h

60 mph

40 km/h

16.8 cm/min

80 km/h

5.8 cm/s

1 Rate I

It took 3 minutes to print out a 120-page document.

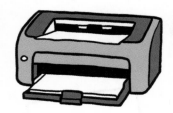

That means the printer can print 40 pages in 1 minute.

3 min ⟶ 120 pages
1 min ⟶ 120 ÷ 3 = 40 pages

We can also write 120 ÷ 3 as $\frac{120}{3}$.

We say that this printer prints at a **rate** of 40 pages in 1 minute.

How many minutes does it take to print a 200-page document?

40 pages ⟶ 1 min
200 pages ⟶ 5 min

1 min ⟶ 40 pages
2 min ⟶ 80 pages
3 min ⟶ 120 pages
4 min ⟶ 160 pages
5 min ⟶ 200 pages

Another way to do it is $\frac{1}{40} \times 200 = 5$.

Alternatively,

×5 ⟮ 40 pages ⟶ 1 min ⟯ ×5
    200 pages ⟶ 5 min

1. In a factory, a machine caps 70 bottles in 1 minute.

   (a) At this rate, how many bottles does it cap in 5 minutes?

   1 min ⟶ 70 bottles

   5 min ⟶ ▢ × 70 = ▢ bottles

   At this rate, the machine caps ▢ bottles in 5 minutes.

   (b) At this rate, how many bottles does it cap in 1 hour?

1 h = 60 min

   1 min ⟶ 70 bottles

   60 min ⟶ ▢ bottles

   1 min ⟶ 70 bottles
   10 min ⟶ 700 bottles
   60 min ⟶ ▢ bottles

   At this rate, the machine caps ▢ bottles in 1 hour.

   A car requires 1 gal of gasoline to travel 25 mi.
   At this rate, find the amount of gasoline required to travel 1 mi.

   25 mi ⟶ 1 gal

   1 mi ⟶ $\frac{1}{25}$ gal

Do you think the answer is more or less than 1 gallon?

   The amount of gasoline required to travel 1 mi is $\frac{1}{25}$ gal.

125

2. A sprinkler sprays 6 in. of water in 4 hours. At this rate, find the amount of water it sprays in 1 hour.

4 h ⟶ 6 in.

1 h ⟶ ▢ in.

The sprinkler sprays ▢ inches of water in 1 hour.

3. A tap fills a 500-cm³ beaker at a rate of 20 cm³ in 1 second. At this rate, how long does it take to fill the beaker to the brim?

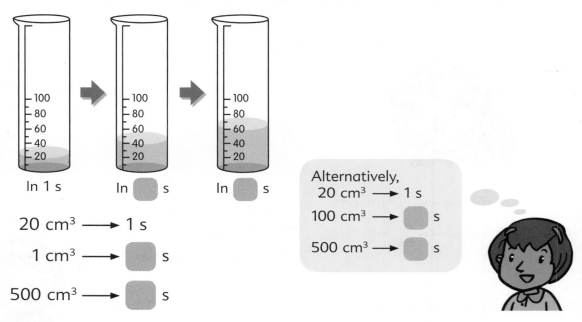

In 1 s   In ▢ s   In ▢ s

20 cm³ ⟶ 1 s

1 cm³ ⟶ ▢ s

500 cm³ ⟶ ▢ s

Alternatively,
20 cm³ ⟶ 1 s
100 cm³ ⟶ ▢ s
500 cm³ ⟶ ▢ s

It takes ▢ seconds to fill the beaker to the brim.

4. A photocopier makes 400 copies in 5 minutes. At this rate, how many copies does it make in 1 minute?

5 min ⟶ 400 copies

1 min ⟶ ▢ copies

We also say that the photocopier makes copies at a rate of ▢ copies **per** minute.

This means it makes ▢ copies in 1 minute.

Exercise 1, pages 94 - 95

5. Water flows into a small pool at a rate of 15 ℓ per second.
Find the volume of water that flows into the pool in 10 minutes.

1 s ⟶ 15 ℓ

1 min ⟶ ▢ ℓ

10 min ⟶ ▢ ℓ

1 min = 60 s

▢ liters of water flows into the pool in 10 minutes.

6.

65¢
per 100 g

(a)

1 kg

1 kg = 1000 g

100 g ⟶ 65¢

1 kg ⟶ $▢

1 kilogram of grapes costs $▢.

(b)

1.32 kg

1 kg = 1000 g
1.32 kg = 1320 g

100 g ⟶ 65¢

1320 g ⟶ $ ▢

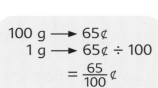

100 g ⟶ 65¢
1 g ⟶ 65¢ ÷ 100
= $\frac{65}{100}$ ¢

So, 1320 g ⟶ $\frac{65}{100}$ ¢ × 1320 g.

1.32 kilogram of grapes cost $ ▢ .

 (c) 100 g ⟶ 65¢

1 g ⟶ ▢

651 g ⟶ $ ▢

651 g

651 grams of grapes cost $ ▢ .

7.

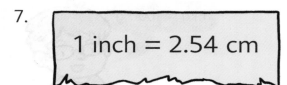

1 inch = 2.54 cm

How long is a 1-ft sandwich in cm?

1 foot = 12 in.

1 in. = 2.54 cm

12 in. = ▢ × 2.54 cm

= ▢ cm

A 1-foot sandwich is ▢ cm.

Exercise 2, pages 96 - 97

1. In a factory, a machine packs cartons of milk into boxes at a rate of 28 boxes per minute. At this rate, how many boxes are packed in 15 minutes?

2. A ferris wheel completes 3 revolutions in an hour. At this rate, how long will it take to complete 18 revolutions?

3. It takes a machine 1.5 h to produce 108 pieces of a car part. Find the rate of producing the car part pieces.

4. Charles made a long distance call that lasted $1\frac{1}{4}$ h.

   The telephone service provider charges 5¢ per minute for the call. How much does Charles have to pay for the call?

5. A solar panel can produce 180 kW of energy per hour. At this rate, how much energy can it produce in 1 minute?

6. (a) How many seconds does it take to print a photograph using this printer?
   (b) Edna prints a dozen photographs. How many minutes does the printer take?

3 photos per minute

7. A pound of tangerines costs $3.

Tangerines

4.2 lb

   How much is the carton of tangerines?

8. Mr. Reyes exchanged US$1000 for Canadian dollars at the rate of US$1 to 1.20 Canadian dollars. How many Canadian dollars did Mr. Reyes get?

9. A thumbdrive takes 8 seconds to write a 36-megabyte file. At this rate, how much data can it write in 1 second?

2 Rate II

1. A worker is paid $12 per hour on weekdays and $15 per hour on weekends.

   (a) He worked 8 hours on Monday.
   Find the amount he was paid on Monday.

   1 h ⟶ $12
   8 h ⟶ $☐

   Should I use $12 per hour or $15 per hour to solve this?

   He was paid $☐ on Monday.

   (b) He was paid $75 on Saturday.
   How many hours did he work on Saturday?

   $15 ⟶ 1 h
   $75 ⟶ ☐ h

   $15 ⟶ 1 h
   $150 ⟶ 10 h
   $75 ⟶ ☐ h

   He worked ☐ hours on Saturday.

2. The parking fees at a parking lot are as follows:

	Parking fees
Peak hours: 9 a.m. to 5 p.m.	$2.50 per hour or part thereof
Off-peak hours: Any other time	$1.50 per hour or part thereof

   Find the parking fees incurred by Mr. Fernando when he parks his car at the following times:

   (a) 10 a.m. to noon

   ```
        $2.50      $2.50
   |-----+-----|-----+-----|
   10 a.m.   11 a.m.    noon
   ```

   Parking fees = 2 × $2.50

   = $☐

(b) 7 p.m. to 10 p.m.

	$◻		$◻		$◻	
7 p.m.		8 p.m.		9 p.m.		10 p.m.

Parking fees = ◻ × $◻

= $◻

(c) 10 p.m. to 1.15 a.m.

	$1.50		$1.50		$1.50		$1.50	
10 p.m.		11 p.m.		midnight		1 a.m.	1.15 a.m.	2 a.m.

Parking fees = ◻ × $◻

= $◻

He paid $1.50 for the last 15 minutes. **'Part thereof'** means Mr. Fernando has to pay $1.50 for anything less than an hour.

What if he parked from 10 p.m. to 1.45 a.m.?

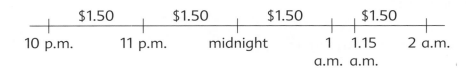

(d) 1.45 p.m. to 4 p.m.

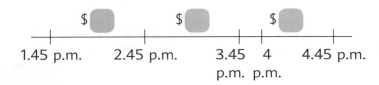

	$◻		$◻		$◻	
1.45 p.m.		2.45 p.m.		3.45 p.m.	4 p.m.	4.45 p.m.

Parking fees = ◻ × $◻

= $◻

131

Exercise 3, pages 99 - 100

3.

> **5 apples for $2**
> **or**
> **1 apple for 50¢**

(a) Find the cost of 3 apples.

1 apple ⟶ 50¢

3 apples ⟶ $☐

3 apples cost $☐.

(b) Find the cost of buying 15 apples.

 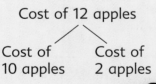

5 apples ⟶ $2

15 apples ⟶ $2 × ☐ = $☐

15 apples cost $☐.

(c) Find the cost of 12 apples.

5 apples ⟶ $2

10 apples ⟶ $2 × ☐ = $☐

Cost of 12 apples
Cost of   Cost of
10 apples   2 apples

2 apples ⟶ 2 × ☐¢ = $☐

12 apples cost $☐.

132

(d) How many apples can you buy with $8?

$2 ⟶ 5 apples

$8 ⟶ ☐ apples

I can buy ☐ apples with $8.

(e) How many apples can you buy with $7?

$2 ⟶ 5 apples

$6 ⟶ ☐ apples

$7
/ \
$6 $1

How many apples can be bought with the remaining $1?

I can buy ☐ apples with $7.

4. These are the prices of admission tickets to an observatory tower.

	Price of a ticket
Adult	$18
Child	$12

(a) Find the cost of tickets for 1 adult and 3 children.

1 child ⟶ $12

3 children ⟶ $☐

$18 + $☐ = $☐

Tickets for 1 adult and 3 children cost $☐.

(b) Find the cost of tickets for 2 adults and 1 child.

1 adult ⟶ $18

2 adults ⟶ $☐

$☐ + $12 = $☐

Tickets for 2 adults and 1 child cost $☐.

(c) Find the combination of tickets that cost $42.

Number of adult tickets	Number of child tickets	Cost
1	1	$30
1	2	$42
2	1	$48
2	2	$☐

Why is it not necessary to check the last row?

(d) Find the combination of tickets that cost $60.

What is the first combination you would check?

Number of adult tickets	Number of child tickets	Cost
☐	☐	☐
☐	☐	☐

Is it possible to have more than one combination of tickets?

5. A taxi company charges the following fare for each trip.

	Fare
For the first 1 mi	$4.90
For every additional 1 mi or part thereof	$2.60

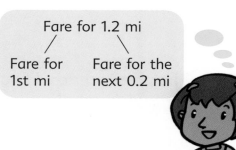

A passenger has to pay $2.60 for every additional 1 mi or less.

(a) Find the fare for a trip of 1.2 mi.

First 1 mi ⟶ $ ☐

Next 0.2 mi ⟶ $ ☐

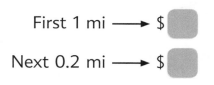

Fare for 1.2 mi
⟋   ⟍
Fare for   Fare for the
1st mi   next 0.2 mi

The fare for a 1.2 mi trip is $ ☐.

(b) Find the fare for a trip of 5 mi.

Fare for 5 mi
⟋   ⟍
Fare for   Fare for the
1st mi   next 4 mi

First 1 mi ⟶ $ ☐

Next 4 mi ⟶ ☐ × $ ☐ = $ ☐

The fare for a 5 mi trip is $ ☐.

(c) Find the fare for a trip of 7.5 mi.

First 1 mi ⟶ $ ☐

Next ☐ mi ⟶ ☐ × $ ☐ = $ ☐

The fare for a 7.5 mi trip is $ ☐.

(d) What is a possible distance a passenger traveled for the fare to be $20?

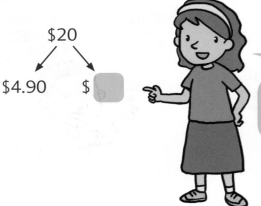

$20

$4.90 $ ☐

What is a possible distance traveled for the fare to be this much?

The passenger could have traveled ☐ mi.

6. Water flows from a tap at the following rate for 10 min.

Time	Rate of flow
First 5 minutes	15 ℓ/min
Next 5 minutes	10 ℓ/min

Find the volume of water flowing from the tap during
(a) the first 2 minutes

First 2 min ⟶ 2 × ☐ = ☐ ℓ

☐ ℓ of water flowed out during the first 2 min.

(b) the last 3 minutes

Last 3 min ⟶ 3 × ☐ = ☐ ℓ

☐ ℓ of water flowed out during the last 3 min.

(c)   the first 6 minutes

First 5 min ⟶ 5 × ☐ = ☐ ℓ

6th min ⟶ ☐ ℓ

☐ ℓ of water flowed out during the first 6 minutes.

(d)   the 3rd to 7th minute

1st min	2nd min	3rd min	4th min	5th min	6th min	7th min	8th min	9th min	10th min

0 min 1 min 2 min 3 min 4 min 5 min 6 min 7 min 8 min 9 min 10 min

3rd to 5th min ⟶ ☐ × ☐ = ☐ ℓ

6th to 7th min ⟶ ☐ × ☐ ℓ = ☐ ℓ

☐ ℓ of water flowed out from the 3rd to 7th min.

7.   A car rental company charges $97 for the use of a car. In addition, it also charges 60¢ for every mile or part thereof traveled. Mr. Li paid $453.60 for renting a car for 3 days. Find the distance Mr. Li traveled with this car.

Exercise 4, pages 101 - 102

1. The table below shows the postage rate for packages.

Weight of packages	Cost
First ounce	$1.17
For every additional ounce or part thereof	$0.17

   (a) What is the cost of mailing a package that weighs 5 ounces?
   (b) Theodora paid $2.36 to mail a package.
        What is the weight of her package?

2. The fares of the Golden Gate ferry are as below:

	Fare
Adult	$7.45
Seniors/Children under 12	$3.70

   (a) What is the total fare for a family consisting of a 38-year-old,
        a 15-year-old and an 8-year-old?
   (b) Another family paid $29.75.
        How many people in this family took the ferry?

3.

	Hotel charges
Weekends (Saturday and Sunday)	$100 per night
Weekdays	$85 per night

   Find the hotel charges to be paid by Mrs. Smith if she
   (a) checks in on Monday and checks out on Thursday,
   (b) checks in on Saturday and checks out on Monday,
   (c) checks in on Sunday and checks out on Wednesday.

4.

   A dozen cookies for $8
   or
   1 cookie for 80¢

   (a) Find the cost of 17 cookies.
   (b) Mia wants 12 cookies. Should she buy them individually or by
        the dozen?

3 Speed

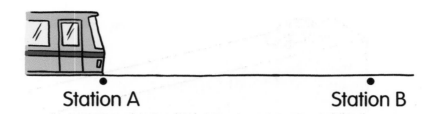

Station A   Station B

The subway train travels 6 miles in 5 minutes in one segment of a journey.

At this rate, how far does the train travel in an hour?

5 min ⟶ 6 mi
10 min ⟶ 12 mi
60 min ⟶ 72 mi

Alternatively,
5 min ⟶ 6 mi
1 min ⟶ $\frac{6}{5}$ mi
60 min ⟶ $\frac{6}{5} \times 60$

We say that the **speed** of the train is 72 miles per hour.

It is written like this.

72 miles/hour

Often, you see it written as 72 mph.

1. In a science experiment, a toy car travels down a slope at a speed of 12 cm/s.

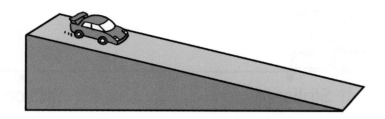

(a) At this speed, how far does the toy car travel in 2 seconds?

1 s ⟶ 12 cm

2 s ⟶ ☐ cm

$2 \times 12 = ?$

It travels ☐ cm in 2 s.

(b) At this speed, how long does the toy car take to travel down a slope 60 cm long?

12 cm ⟶ 1 s

1 cm ⟶ ☐ s

60 cm ⟶ ☐ s

Alternatively,

× ☐ ⟮ 12 cm ⟶ 1 s
       60 cm ⟶ ☐ s ⟯ × ☐

It takes ☐ s to travel down a slope 60 cm long.

2. A cable car at a ski resort travels a 500-m segment in 50 seconds.
    (a) At this speed, how long does it take to travel 1 km?

$$500 \text{ m} \longrightarrow 50 \text{ s}$$
$$1 \text{ km} \longrightarrow \boxed{} \text{ s}$$

1 km = 1000 m

Alternatively,
$$500 \text{ m} \longrightarrow 50 \text{ s}$$
$$1 \text{ m} \longrightarrow \frac{50}{500} = \frac{1}{10}$$
$$1 \text{ km} \longrightarrow \frac{1}{10} \times 1000 = \boxed{} \text{ s}$$

It takes $\boxed{}$ s to travel 1 km.

(b) Find the speed of the cable car in km/h over this 500-m segment.

$$50 \text{ s} \longrightarrow 500 \text{ m}$$
$$10 \text{ s} \longrightarrow \boxed{} \text{ m}$$
$$1 \text{ min} \longrightarrow \boxed{} \text{ m}$$
$$1 \text{ h} \longrightarrow \boxed{} \text{ m}$$
$$1 \text{ h} \longrightarrow \boxed{} \text{ km}$$

1 min = 60 s

Alternatively,
$$50 \text{ s} \longrightarrow 500 \text{ m}$$
$$1 \text{ s} \longrightarrow \frac{500}{50} = 10 \text{ m}$$
$$1 \text{ min} \longrightarrow 10 \times \boxed{}$$

The speed of the cable car over this 500-m segment is $\boxed{}$ km/h.

Exercise 5, pages 103 - 104

PRACTICE C

1.

		Distance traveled	Time taken	Speed
(a)	Space shuttle	36,000 mi	5 h	☐ mph
(b)	Subway	12 km	8 min	☐ km/h
(c)	Elevator	70 m	$\frac{1}{2}$ min	☐ km/h

For certain segments of a movement, the speed of an object can stay the same.

2.

		Speed	Distance traveled	Time taken
(a)	Treadmill	25 m/s	100 m	☐ s
(b)	Cruise ship	24 mph	15 mi	☐ min
(c)	Airplane	900 km/h	675,000 m	☐ min

3.

	Speed	Time taken	Distance traveled
(a) Gondola	1.5 m/s	90 s	▢ m
(b) Remote-controlled car	36 mph	40 min	▢ mi
(c) Conveyor belt	0.72 km/h	8 min	▢ m

4.   A conveyor belt at the airport moves at a speed of 2 m in 10 seconds. Find the speed of a luggage on this conveyor belt in m/s.

5.   An elevator moves at a constant speed of 2 m/s for most of its journey. Estimate the time needed to travel up a 12-story building in this elevator.

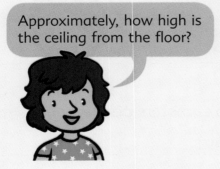

Approximately, how high is the ceiling from the floor?

Approximately, how tall is a 12-story building?

4 Average Speed

Marcela walked 100 m in 25 s.
Nellie ran the same distance in 15 s.

Marcela did not move at the same speed throughout the 100 meters.
Neither did Nellie.

> The information we have is not enough for us to know their speeds throughout the journey.

$$25 \text{ s} \longrightarrow 100 \text{ m}$$
$$1 \text{ s} \longrightarrow 100 \div 25 = \boxed{} \text{ m}$$

On average, Marcela walked at a speed of 4 meters per second.
We say Marcela's **average speed** is 4 m/s.

$$15 \text{ s} \longrightarrow 100 \text{ m}$$
$$1 \text{ s} \longrightarrow \frac{100}{15} = \boxed{} \text{ m}$$

On average, Nellie ran at a speed of $6\frac{2}{3}$ meters per second.

We say Nellie's average speed is $6\frac{2}{3}$ m/s.

1.

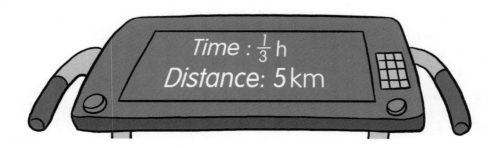

Mr. Carlos ran 5 km in $\frac{1}{3}$ h on the treadmill. Calculate his average speed on the treadmill in kilometers per hour.

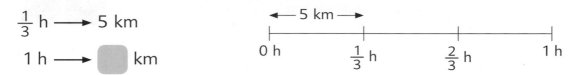

$\frac{1}{3}$ h ⟶ 5 km

1 h ⟶ ▢ km

Mr. Carlos' average speed on the treadmill was ▢ km/h.

2. A van took 36 minutes to travel from one town to another.
   The towns are 54 km apart.
   Calculate the van's average speed in km per hour.

On average,

36 min ⟶ 54 km

6 min ⟶ ▢ km

1 h ⟶ ▢ km.

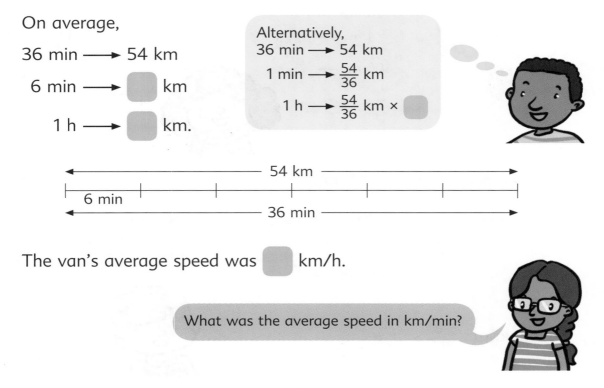

Alternatively,
36 min ⟶ 54 km

1 min ⟶ $\frac{54}{36}$ km

1 h ⟶ $\frac{54}{36}$ km × ▢

The van's average speed was ▢ km/h.

What was the average speed in km/min?

3. The average speed of a car traveling from Town A to Town B was 60 mph. Town A is 36 miles from Town B. Find the time the car took to travel from Town A to Town B.

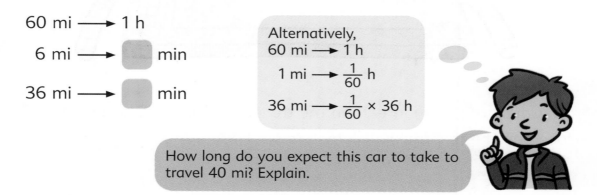

60 mi ⟶ 1 h

6 mi ⟶ ▢ min

36 mi ⟶ ▢ min

Alternatively,
60 mi ⟶ 1 h

1 mi ⟶ $\frac{1}{60}$ h

36 mi ⟶ $\frac{1}{60}$ × 36 h

How long do you expect this car to take to travel 40 mi? Explain.

The car took ▢ min to travel from Town A to Town B.

4. The average speed of a sprinter in a 400-m race was 8 m/s. How much faster would he run the race if his average speed was 10 m/s?

If his average speed was 8 m/s,

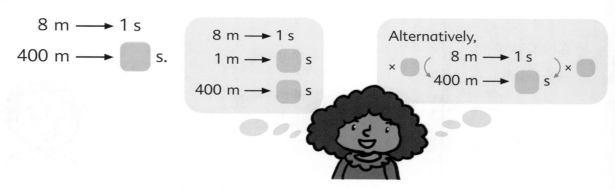

8 m ⟶ 1 s

400 m ⟶ ▢ s.

8 m ⟶ 1 s

1 m ⟶ ▢ s

400 m ⟶ ▢ s

Alternatively,

× ▢ (8 m ⟶ 1 s / 400 m ⟶ ▢ s) × ▢

If his average speed was 10 m/s,

10 m ⟶ 1 s

400 m ⟶ ▢ s.

10 m ⟶ 1 s

1 m ⟶ ▢ s

400 m ⟶ ▢

Alternatively,

10 m ⟶ 1 s

× ▢ (400 m ⟶ ▢ s) × ▢

He would run ▢ s faster.

5. It is given that the average speed of a subway train is 72 km/h. At this average speed, how far does it travel in

(a) $\frac{1}{12}$ hour?

1 h ⟶ 72 km

$\frac{1}{12}$ h ⟶ ▢ km

← ? →

⟵——————— 72 km ———————⟶

It travels ▢ km in $\frac{1}{12}$ hour.

(b) 12 minutes?

60 min ⟶ 72 km

12 min ⟶ ▢ km

It travels ▢ km in 12 minutes.

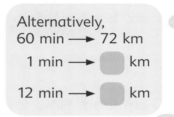

Alternatively,
60 min ⟶ 72 km
1 min ⟶ ▢ km
12 min ⟶ ▢ km

÷ ▢ (60 min ⟶ 72 km / 12 min ⟶ ▢ s) ÷ ▢

6.

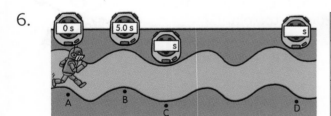

Segment	Distance (cm)
AB	125
BC	75

(a) Calculate the robot's average speed when it traveled from Point A to Point B.

5.0 s ⟶ ▢ cm

1.0 s ⟶ ▢ cm

Calculate its average speed in m/s.

Its average speed was ▢ cm/s.

(b) The robot's average speed when it traveled from Point A to Point C was found to be 16 cm/s.
What time should the stopwatch at Point C show?

16 cm ⟶ 1 s

☐ cm ⟶ ☐ s

125 + 75 = ☐

The stopwatch at Point C shows ☐ s.

Calculate the robot's average speed from Point B to Point C.

(c) AD is 400 cm long. How fast should the robot travel from Point C to Point D for its average speed from Point A to Point D to be 12.5 cm/s?

12.5 cm ⟶ 1 s
25 cm ⟶ 2 s

100 cm ⟶ ☐ s

400 cm ⟶ ☐ s

Can you find the **time** the robot takes to travel from Point C to Point D?

The robot should travel from Point C to Point D in ☐ s.

7. Ben left Town X 30 min earlier than Paul. Ben reached Town Y 50 min later than Paul. When Paul reached Town Y, Ben had completed $\frac{4}{5}$ of the journey and was 75 km from Town Y. Find Paul's average speed in km/h.

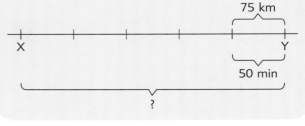

In this problem, we assume that Ben's and Paul's speed did not change.

In reality, it is impossible for Ben's and Paul's speed not to change. But we are assuming this to make the calculation manageable.

In high school, we will learn more mathematics to allow us to solve this problem without having to make this assumption.

Ben took [ ] minutes for 75 km.

Ben took [ ] minutes for $\frac{1}{5}$ of the journey.

Ben took [ ] minutes for the entire journey.

Ben's total time is [ ] minutes.

75 km

X ────────────────────── Y

50 min

?

75 km

X ────────────────────── Y

?

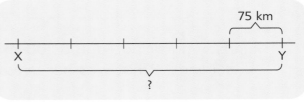

To calculate Paul's average speed,

Paul's total **distance** = [ ]

Paul's total time = [ ]

Paul's average speed = [ ]

Ben took [ ] min less than Paul.

Paul's average speed is [ ] km/h.

Exercise 6, pages 105 - 106

1.

		Average speed	Time taken	Distance traveled
(b)	Hippopotamus	30 km/h	24 min	☐ km
(c)	Lion	80 km/h	$\frac{1}{2}$ min	☐ m

2.

		Distance traveled	Time taken	Average speed
(b)	Woman jumping over a hurdle on a track	400 m	50 s	☐ m/min
(c)	Three athletes running a 100-m race	100 m	10 s	☐ km/h

3.

		Average speed	Distance traveled	Time taken
(b)	Subway	40 km/h	12 km	☐ min
(c)	Tram	9 km/h	750 m	☐ min

4. Lindsay participated in a 100-m race. She completed the race in 12 seconds. What was her average speed per minute?

5. Mr. Spelling drove from City A to City B at an average speed of 108 km/h. He took 4 hours to complete his journey and this includes a 20-minute break. What is the distance between City A and City B?

6. Gerard and Chelsea both drove from Town A to Town B. Chelsea started her journey before Gerard. Driving at an average speed of 80 mph, Gerard arrived at Town B in 45 minutes. Chelsea drove at an average speed of 45 mph and arrived at Town B at the same time as Gerard. How many minutes did Chelsea start her journey before Gerard?

REVIEW 4

1. A fraction $\frac{x}{y}$ is $\frac{3}{7}$.

   Write each ratio:

   (a) $x : y$
   (b) $x : x + y$

   What if $\frac{x}{y}$ is written as $\frac{6}{14}$ or $\frac{18}{21}$ which are not in the simplest form?

2.

   1 in 4 people say that they would buy this newly launched magazine.

   (a) Find the ratio of people who say that they would buy the magazine to the total number of people interviewed.
   (b) What percent of the people interviewed said that they would buy the magazine?

3. After a library bought new books, its collection increased by 20%.

   (a) Find the ratio of the number of new books to the original number of books.
   (b) What fraction of the books in the library are new books?

4. Stefan thinks of 3 numbers.
   The ratio of $a : b$ is $2 : 3$.
   The ratio of $a : c$ is $4 : 5$.

   (a) Find the ratio of $b : c$.
   (b) Find the values of b and c if a is 20.

   Which of the two numbers, b or c, is closest to 28? Can you tell by looking at the ratio?

5. Al draws a trapezoid and uses a copier to reduce and enlarge it.

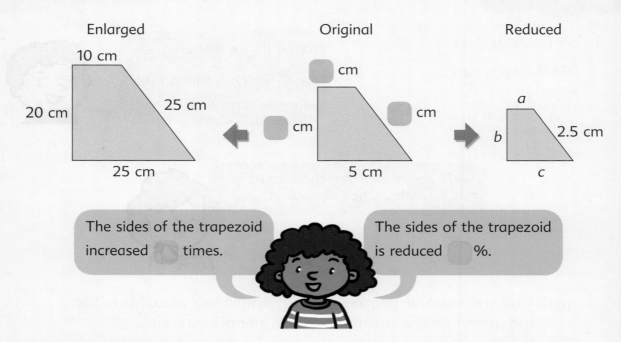

Enlarged   Original   Reduced

The sides of the trapezoid increased ☐ times.

The sides of the trapezoid is reduced ☐ %.

(a) Find the missing numbers.
(b) Find the values of *a*, *b* and *c*.
(c) Find the perimeter of the smallest trapezoid.

6. The late charges for the rental of a DVD are $3 for the first 4 days and $1 per day subsequently.

(a) Barlo was late by a week. Find the amount he paid.
(b) Crystal was late by more than 4 days and paid $x. Find an expression for the number of days which she was late in returning the DVD.
(c) Dave was late by 10 days. Find the amount he paid in two different ways.

7. Sam and Terry ran on the treadmill. Sam started 10 minutes before Terry. Terry finished 5 minutes before Sam. They both ran the same distance. When Terry finished, Sam had completed $\frac{4}{5}$ of the journey and still had $\frac{1}{2}$ mi more to go.

(a) Whose speed was faster?
(b) Find Sam's speed.
(c) Find Terry's speed.

152

Review 4, pages 109 - 112

GLOSSARY

Word/Phrase	Meaning
algebraic equation	An **algebraic equation** is a mathematical statement that has two quantities joined by an equal sign. At least one of the quantities is unknown. $x + 4 = 13$ and $\frac{2}{5}m = 20$ are **algebraic equations**.
algebraic expression	An **algebraic expression** is an expression that contains at least one letter to represent unknown numbers. $4x$, $2 + 9w$, $3m - 5n$ are **algebraic expressions**.
• **algebraic expression in one variable**	An **algebraic expression in one variable** is an expression that contains only one letter to represent unknown numbers.
• **algebraic expression in two variables**	An **algebraic expression in two variables** is an expression that contains two letters to represent unknown numbers.
• **algebraic expression in three variables**	An **algebraic expression in three variables** is an expression that contains three letters to represent unknown numbers.
bar model	A **bar model** is a pictorial representation used as a visual aid to solve word problems. It is represented by rectangular blocks.
commission	A **commission** is a percentage of the value of sales made by a salesperson.
consecutive whole numbers	**Consecutive whole numbers** are numbers that follow one another in order. 17, 18, 19, 20 are **consecutive whole numbers**.

Word/Phrase	Meaning
decimal	A **decimal** is a number that represents a fraction with a denominator of 10, 100, 1000, and so on. $0.5 = \frac{5}{10}, \quad 0.11 = \frac{11}{100}$
denominator	The **denominator** is the bottom number in a fraction. It indicates the number of parts the whole is divided into. $\frac{2}{7}$ ⟵ **denominator**
discount	A **discount** is an amount that is subtracted from the normal price of an item.
distance	**Distance** is the length between two points or objects.
enlarge (proportionately)	To **enlarge proportionately** means to increase the size of an object without affecting its shape.
express	To **express** something in a certain way means to write it in the form that was asked. To **express** 0.28 as a fraction means to write 0.28 in the fraction form.
factor	An integer that divides into another without any remainder. $3 \times 4 = 12$ 3 and 4 are **factors** of 12.

Word/Phrase	Meaning
fraction	A way of representing equal parts of a whole or equal parts of a set. $\frac{1}{3}$ of a rectangle is shaded. $\frac{1}{3}$ of a set of rectangles is shaded.
graph	A **graph** is a drawing or diagram used to show information about sets of data.
• **graph of functions**	A diagram showing how one variable varies as another variable is changed.
horizontal	A line is **horizontal** if it is drawn from side to side.
• **horizontal number line**	A **horizontal number line** is a straight line that is marked with numbers from left to right, at regular intervals. $-3 \quad -2 \quad -1 \quad 0 \quad 1 \quad 2 \quad 3$
hundredths	Parts of one whole that is divided into 100 equal parts. **9 hundredths**

Word/Phrase	Meaning
integer	An **integer** is a positive or negative whole number (including zero). −8, −1, 0, 5 and 21 are examples of **integers**.
interest	**Interest** is the amount of money earned from savings or investments.
multiple • **common multiple** • **least common multiple**	A **multiple** is the product of two factors of a number. A **common multiple** is a number which is a multiple of each of the given numbers in a set. **Least common multiple** is the smallest number that is a common multiple of two numbers. **Multiples** of 2: 2, 4, **6**, 8, 10, **12**, 14, 16, **18**, … **Multiples** of 3: 3, **6**, 9, **12**, 15, **18**, 21, … 6, 12 and 18 are **common multiples** of 2 and 3. 6 is the **least common multiple** of 2 and 3.
negative number	A **negative number** is less than zero and written with a negative sign in front of it. −6 is **negative** six. $-\frac{1}{4}$ is **negative** one-quarter. −2.1 is **negative** two point one.
numerator	The **numerator** is the top number in a fraction. It indicates the number of equal parts that are described by the fraction. $\frac{5}{6}$ ⟵ numberator

Word/Phrase	Meaning
part thereof	The parking fee at a parking lot for off-peak hours is $1.50 per hour or part thereof. **Part thereof** means $1.50 needs to be paid for anything less than an hour.
per	For each.
percentage	A **percentage** is a ratio or fraction with a denominator of 100.
• **percentage change**	**Percentage change** represents the relative change between the new value and the original value of a quantity or item.
• **percent**	**Percent** means out of 100. The symbol for percent is %.
• **percent decrease**	**Percent decrease** of a value measures how that value decreases, as a percent of its original value.
• **percent increase**	**Percent increase** of a value measures how that value increases, as a percent of its original value.
proportion	Two quantities are in **proportion** if they increase or decrease in the same ratio.
rate	1. A quantity measured with respect to another measured quantity; e.g. a rate of speed of 60 miles an hour. 2. A measure of a part with respect to a whole; a proportion; e.g. a tax rate. 3. The cost per unit of a commodity or service; e.g. postal rates.
ratio	**Ratio** is the comparison of two quantities expressed in the form $x : y$.

Word/Phrase	Meaning
simplest form (lowest form)	A fraction is said to be in its **simplest form** if the numerator and denominator have only 1 as their common factor. The simplest form of $\frac{12}{20}$ is $\frac{3}{5}$. A ratio is said to be in its **simplest form** if the two quantities have only 1 as their common factor. The simplest form of $8:28$ is $2:7$.
solution (problem)	The answer to the problem.
solution (equation)	Value or values of the variables that, when substituted into the equation, will make the equation true.
solve	To **solve** means to find the answer to a problem or the value of the variable that will make the equation true.
speed	**Speed** is a measure of how far an object can travel in a given unit of time.
• **average speed**	The average speed of an object is found by considering only the total time taken by the object and the total distance traveled.
sum	The result from adding numbers.
table	A set of data or information that is organized in rows and columns.

Word/Phrase	Meaning
tax	An amount of money paid to the government to help fund government expenditures or services.
• **sales tax**	A tax imposed on goods purchased and services used. It is usually added to the item's cost.
• **income tax**	A tax imposed based on one's income.
tenths	Parts of one whole that is divided into 10 equal parts.

2 **tenths**

Word/Phrase	Meaning
time	The duration or interval between two events. It is usually measured in seconds, minutes, hours, and so on.
vertical	A **vertical** line is straight up and down.
• **vertical number line**	A **vertical number line** is a straight line that is marked with numbers from down to up, at regular intervals.

$$2$$
$$1$$
$$0$$
$$-1$$

Index